SO-AGW-848

OFFICE

Voodoo

Tailor your torture with
138 tear-out hex sheets

Enchanted by Madam Bontecou

STERLING INNOVATION
An imprint of Sterling Publishing Co., Inc.

New York / London
www.sterlingpublishing.com

STERLING, the Sterling logo, STERLING INNOVATION,
and the Sterling Innovation logo are registered trademarks
of Sterling Publishing Co., Inc.

10 9 8 7 6 5 4 3 2 1

Published by Sterling Publishing Co., Inc.
387 Park Avenue South, New York, NY 10016
© 2010 by Sterling Publishing Co., Inc.

Distributed in Canada by Sterling Publishing
c/o Canadian Manda Group, 165 Dufferin Street
Toronto, Ontario, Canada M6K 3H6
Distributed in the United Kingdom by GMC Distribution Services
Castle Place, 166 High Street, Lewes, East Sussex, England BN7 1XU
Distributed in Australia by Capricorn Link (Australia) Pty. Ltd.
P.O. Box 704, Windsor, NSW 2756, Australia

Printed in China
All rights reserved

Sterling ISBN 978-1-4027-7508-6

Design by Yeon J. Kim
Written by Katherine Furman

For information about custom editions, special sales, premium and
corporate purchases, please contact Sterling Special Sales
Department at 800-805-5489 or specialsales@sterlingpublishing.com.

CONTENTS

INTRODUCTION

Do you have problems at the office? Is your boss an idiot? Are your co-workers loud, lazy, and generally unbearable? Maybe pointless meetings have destroyed your will to live, or the technical support guy took three weeks to tell you he has no idea why your computer gives you a mild electrical shock each time you touch the mouse.

If you tried all the ordinary avenues for solving problems—making reasonable requests of your fellow employees, filing complaints with HR, drinking yourself stupid before work—all to no avail, then *Office Voodoo* is here to rescue you!

Voodoo dolls have been used for centuries because life is not fair, the world is not balanced, and total friggen jerks are usually the ones to get ahead. These dolls are made to exact a little justice in an arbitrary universe. They control people without all the fuss and muss of direct contact. They get you your way without anyone knowing it was you that made the way.

Traditionally, you needed a doll, a pin, and a personal belonging to make some voodoo. But *Office Voodoo* doesn't require that much effort—you've got enough to do already. The only things you need to animate the powers of your paper voodoo dolls are a pen and a thirst for retribution (though attaching the offender's business card to their doll couldn't hurt).

By beseeching the office gods to administer comeuppances, you can make your work life a pleasure—or at least tolerable— from the comfort of your ergonomically incorrect desk chair. Each problematic person in your office has a likeness in this book, and all you have to do is check off the circle connected with the appropriate curse to inflict retribution. You can transfix your boss into giving you that well-deserved raise, blight that loud jerk down the hall with laryngitis, or make sure that fink who's been taking credit for your work is caught red-handed with stolen office supplies. How did that Swingline get in Mr. Mitchell's briefcase? Only you and the real powers-that-be will know. But how do the spirits get wind of your incantations without priestesses and sacrificial chickens? Easy. Each page of *Office Voodoo* is a mystical memo to the deities of the corporate ladder, the saints of the server, and the demons of email. The corporate gods know nothing of entrails and tea leaves, but they certainly understand the importance of processing official paperwork. So go ahead, find the doll for the person most deserving of a bit of bad luck, a broken chair, or a grave cell phone misfortune, and ensure they get what's coming to them.

Madam Bontecou

YOUR BOSS

Your boss is a very important person (or sometimes, unfortunately, persons) in your life, who dictates your day-to-day existence.

They hired/enslaved you, granting them the power to watchdog your every move. They keep tabs on when you come in, when you call out, and when you go on vacation. They make more money than you, get more recognition than you, and have a sweeter office than you. They blame you for mistakes, take credit for your ideas, and worsen the ever-present pain in your ass that no cream can alleviate. Isn't it time you made this relationship a two-way street?

Take back a little control by clouding your boss's vision of you with a glowing halo of competence. If they're about to attribute your work to themselves in a big meeting, then tie their tongue during the presentation. Or maybe you just need a good laugh and want to see some toilet paper gets stuck to their heel for an impossible amount of time.

Just pick a doll, check a circle, and kick up your feet as the magic unfolds.

OFFENDER _____

OFFENSE _____

VOODOO RETRIBUTION _____

Blind to days
when you arrive late

Permanent amnesia for any
issues with your "performance"

Tongue atrophies
in all attempts to pass
blame your way

Icy **heart melts**
during yearly reivew

Compelled to
sign-off on
all expense reports

Overcome with
urge to perform the
Moon Dance
when approaching
your desk

*** Check all that apply. Fill in your own spells and incantations. ***

9

YOUR HEXES _____
_____
_____

MORE CURSES _____
_____
_____
_____

Deaf to things said behind the back

Ass is hyper-sensative to kissing

10

OFFENDER _____

OFFENSE _____

VOODOO RETRIBUTION _____

Permanent amnesia for any issues with your "performance"

Blind to days when you arrive late

Tongue atrophies in all attempts to pass blame your way

Icy **heart melts** during yearly reivew

Compelled to **sign-off** on all expense reports

Overcome with urge to perform the **Moon Dance** when approaching your desk

*** Check all that apply. Fill in your own spells and incantations. ***

YOUR HEXES _____
_____
_____

MORE CURSES _____
_____
_____
_____

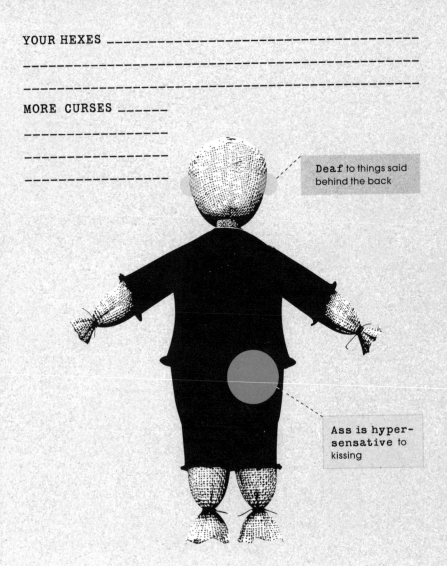

Deaf to things said behind the back

Ass is hyper-sensative to kissing

12

OFFENDER _____

OFFENSE _____

VOODOO RETRIBUTION _____

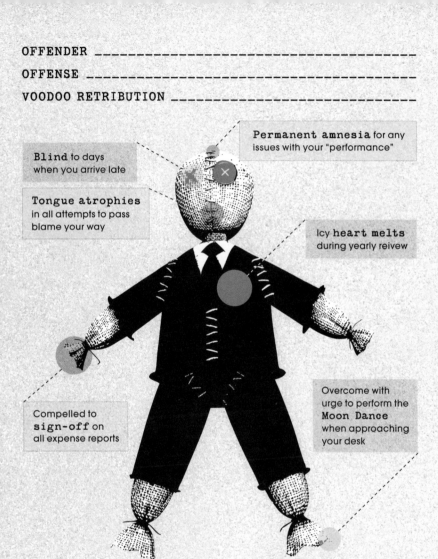

Permanent amnesia for any issues with your "performance"

Blind to days when you arrive late

Tongue atrophies in all attempts to pass blame your way

Icy **heart melts** during yearly reivew

Compelled to **sign-off** on all expense reports

Overcome with urge to perform the **Moon Dance** when approaching your desk

*** Check all that apply. Fill in your own spells and incantations. ***

YOUR HEXES _____

_____

_____

MORE CURSES _____

_____

_____

_____

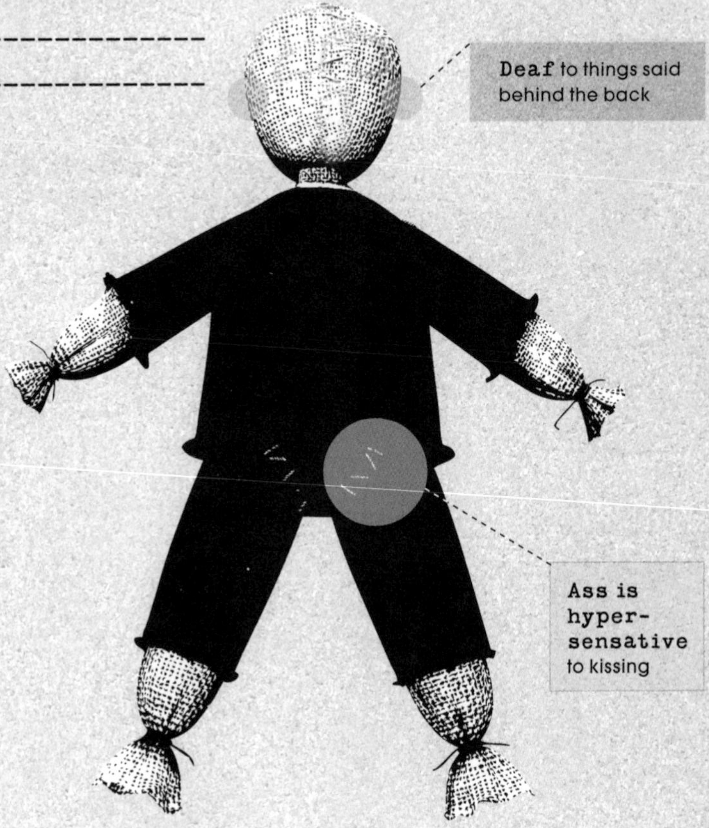

Deaf to things said behind the back

Ass is hyper-sensative to kissing

OFFENDER _____

OFFENSE _____

VOODOO RETRIBUTION _____

Permanent amnesia for any issues with your "performance"

Blind to days when you arrive late

Tongue atrophies in all attempts to pass blame your way

Icy **heart melts** during yearly reivew

Compelled to **sign-off** on all expense reports

Overcome with urge to perform the **Moon Dance** when approaching your desk

*** Check all that apply. Fill in your own spells and incantations. ***

YOUR HEXES _____

MORE CURSES _____
_____
_____
_____

Deaf to things said
behind the back

Ass is hyper-
sensitive to
kissing

OFFENDER _____

OFFENSE _____

VOODOO RETRIBUTION _____

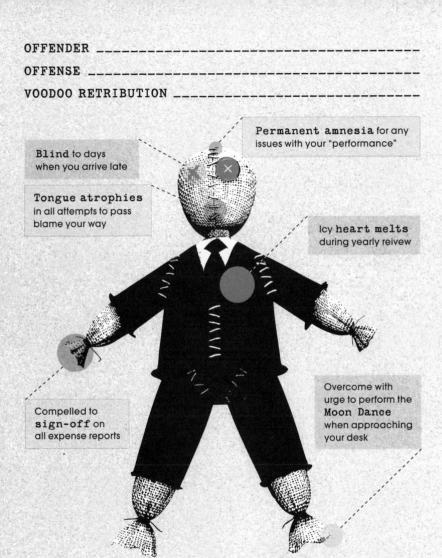

Permanent amnesia for any issues with your "performance"

Blind to days when you arrive late

Tongue atrophies in all attempts to pass blame your way

Icy **heart melts** during yearly reivew

Compelled to **sign-off** on all expense reports

Overcome with urge to perform the **Moon Dance** when approaching your desk

*** Check all that apply. Fill in your own spells and incantations. ***

YOUR HEXES _____

_____

_____

MORE CURSES _____

_____

_____

_____

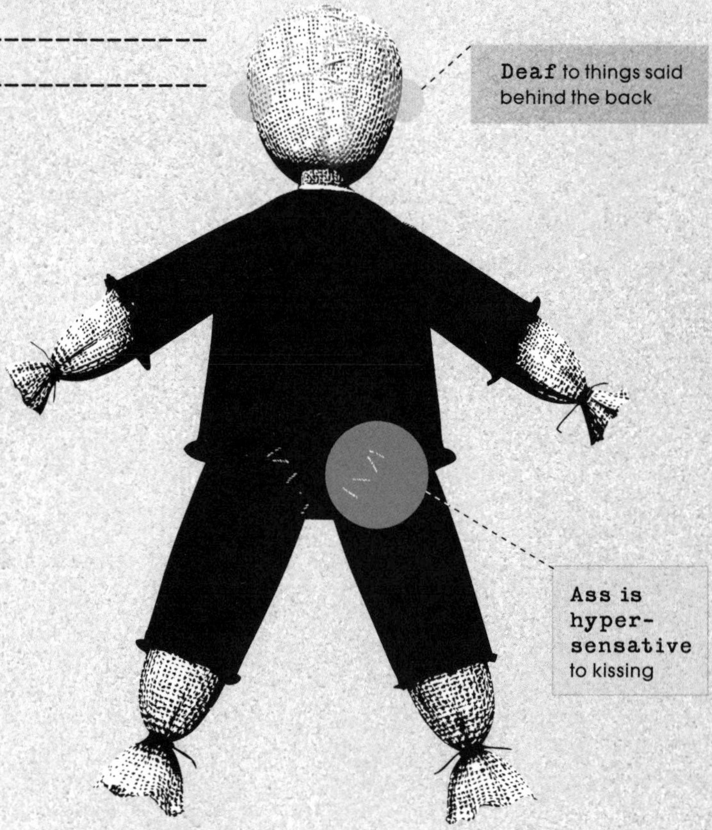

Deaf to things said
behind the back

Ass is
hyper-
sensative
to kissing

OFFENDER _____

OFFENSE _____

VOODOO RETRIBUTION _____

Permanent amnesia for any issues with your "performance"

Blind to days when you arrive late

Tongue atrophies in all attempts to pass blame your way

Icy **heart melts** during yearly reivew

Compelled to **sign-off** on all expense reports

Overcome with urge to perform the **Moon Dance** when approaching your desk

*** Check all that apply. Fill in your own spells and incantations. ***

YOUR HEXES _
_ _
_ _

MORE CURSES _ _ _ _ _ _ _
_ _ _ _ _ _ _ _ _ _ _ _ _ _ _ _ _
_ _ _ _ _ _ _ _ _ _ _ _ _ _ _ _ _
_ _ _ _ _ _ _ _ _ _ _ _ _ _ _

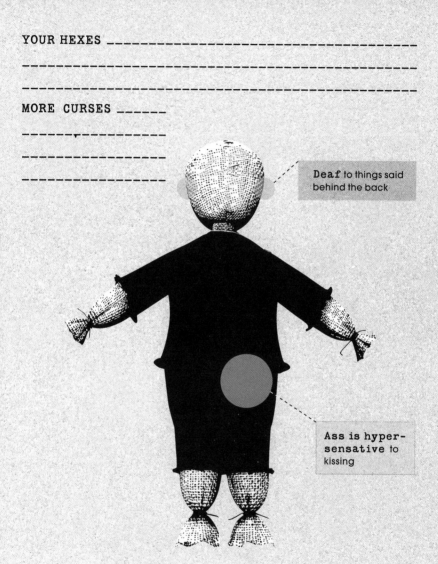

Deaf to things said
behind the back

**Ass is hyper-
sensitive** to
kissing

OFFENDER _____

OFFENSE _____

VOODOO RETRIBUTION _____

Permanent amnesia for any issues with your "performance"

Blind to days when you arrive late

Tongue atrophies in all attempts to pass blame your way

Icy **heart melts** during yearly reievw

Compelled to **sign-off** on all expense reports

Overcome with urge to perform the **Moon Dance** when approaching your desk

*** Check all that apply. Fill in your own spells and incantations. ***

YOUR HEXES _____
_____
_____

MORE CURSES _____
_____
_____
_____

Deaf to things said
behind the back

Ass is
hyper-
sensative
to kissing

OFFENDER _____

OFFENSE _____

VOODOO RETRIBUTION _____

Permanent amnesia for any issues with your "performance"

Blind to days when you arrive late

Tongue atrophies in all attempts to pass blame your way

Icy **heart melts** during yearly reivew

Compelled to **sign-off** on all expense reports

Overcome with urge to perform the **Moon Dance** when approaching your desk

*** Check all that apply. Fill in your own spells and incantations. ***

YOUR HEXES _____
_____
_____

MORE CURSES _____
_____
_____
_____

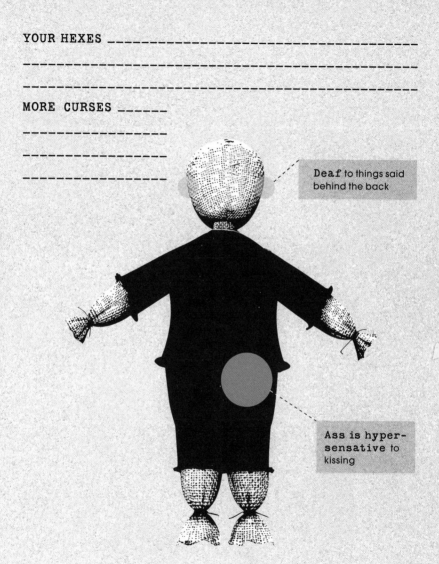

Deaf to things said behind the back

Ass is hyper-sensative to kissing

OFFENDER _____

OFFENSE _____

VOODOO RETRIBUTION _____

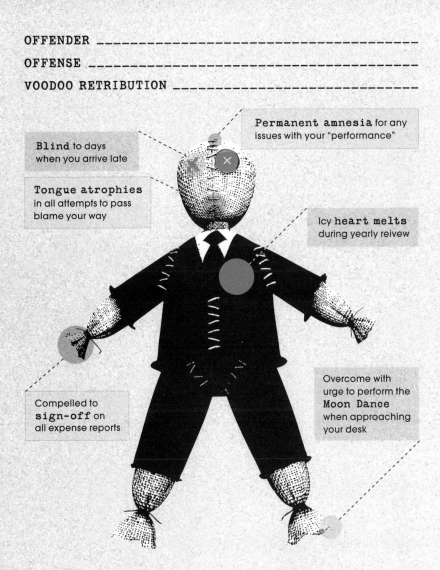

Blind to days when you arrive late

Permanent amnesia for any issues with your "performance"

Tongue atrophies in all attempts to pass blame your way

Icy **heart melts** during yearly reivew

Compelled to **sign-off** on all expense reports

Overcome with urge to perform the **Moon Dance** when approaching your desk

*** Check all that apply. Fill in your own spells and incantations. ***

YOUR HEXES _____

_____

_____

MORE CURSES _____

_____

_____

_____

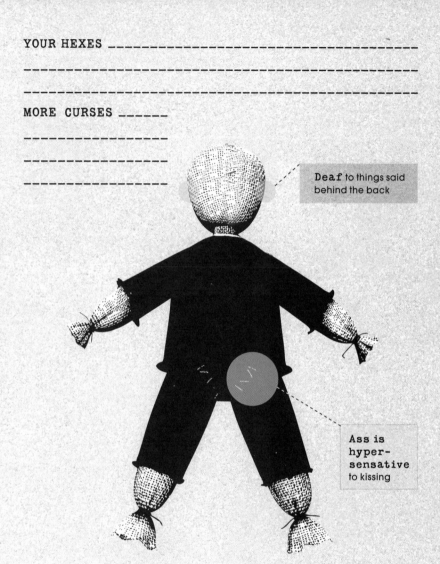

Deaf to things said behind the back

Ass is hyper-sensative to kissing

OFFENDER _____

OFFENSE _____

VOODOO RETRIBUTION _____

Blind to days when you arrive late

Permanent amnesia for any issues with your "performance"

Tongue atrophies in all attempts to pass blame your way

Icy **heart melts** during yearly reivew

Compelled to **sign-off** on all expense reports

Overcome with urge to perform the **Moon Dance** when approaching your desk

*** Check all that apply. Fill in your own spells and incantations. ***

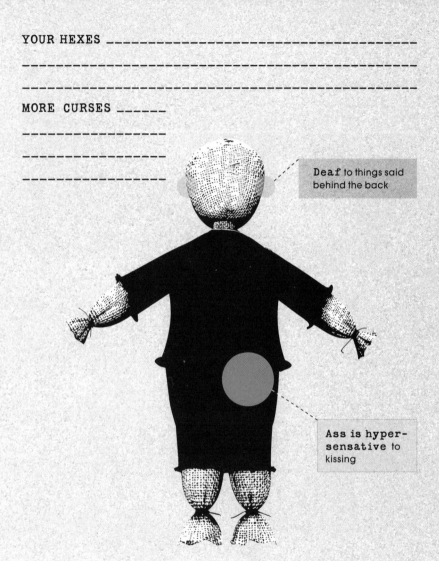

YOUR HEXES _____
_____
_____

MORE CURSES _____
_____
_____
_____

Deaf to things said behind the back

Ass is hyper-sensative to kissing

28

OFFENDER _____

OFFENSE _____

VOODOO RETRIBUTION _____

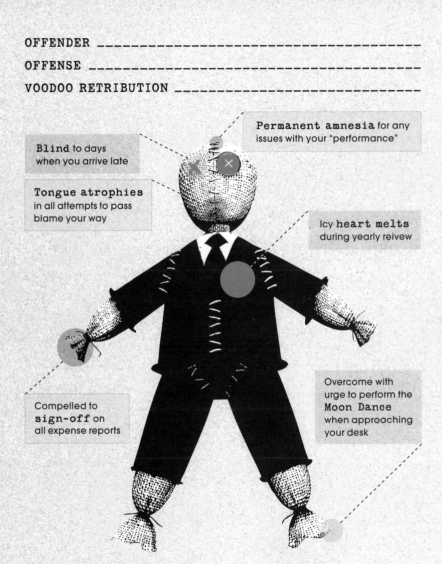

Permanent amnesia for any issues with your "performance"

Blind to days when you arrive late

Tongue atrophies in all attempts to pass blame your way

Icy **heart melts** during yearly reivew

Compelled to **sign-off** on all expense reports

Overcome with urge to perform the **Moon Dance** when approaching your desk

*** Check all that apply. Fill in your own spells and incantations. ***

MORE CURSES _____

_____

_____

_____

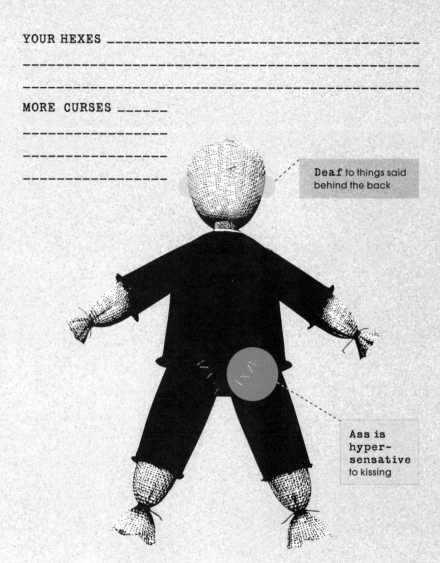

Deaf to things said
behind the back

**Ass is
hyper-
sensitive**
to kissing

CEO (BIG CHEESE)

Do you pee your pants just a little each time the CEO/Big Cheese walks by wearing a sharply pressed suit and determined glare?

Does your blood percolate like the offensive coffee in the break room when you think about how many months of your rent their watch would pay for? Who do they think they are anyway, with their company cars, unchecked expense accounts, and fancy-schmancy corner offices?

Now's your chance to exact some payback while cowering at your desk. Payback for what? Payback for their lives being seemingly better than yours, even though they're probably not since they're going bald from stress. Or at least they will be once you're done with them—wink wink. You can cause them international embarrassment, make their pockets spring open at bonus time, or inflict whatever retribution you see fit.

OFFENDER _____

OFFENSE _____

VOODOO RETRIBUTION _____

_____

_____

_____

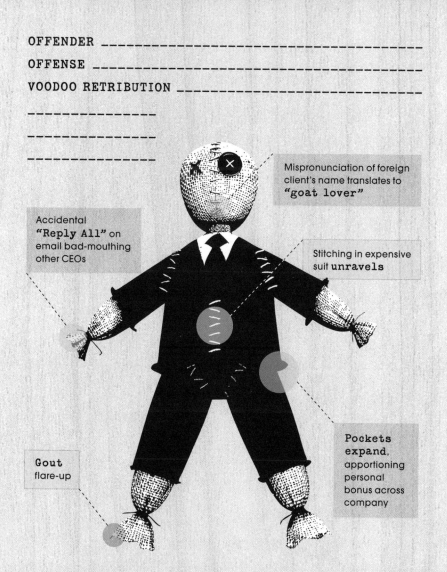

Mispronunciation of foreign client's name translates to **"goat lover"**

Accidental **"Reply All"** on email bad-mouthing other CEOs

Stitching in expensive suit **unravels**

Pockets expand, apportioning personal bonus across company

Gout flare-up

*** Check all that apply. Fill in your own spells and incantations. ***

33

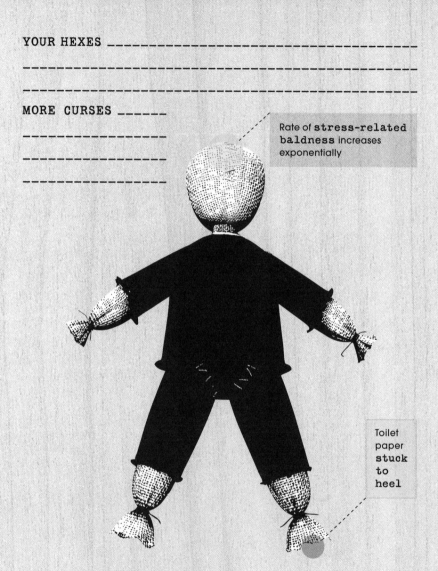

YOUR HEXES _____
_____
_____

MORE CURSES _____
_____
_____
_____

Rate of **stress-related baldness** increases exponentially

Toilet
paper
**stuck
to
heel**

34

OFFENDER _____

OFFENSE _____

VOODOO RETRIBUTION _____

_____

_____

_____

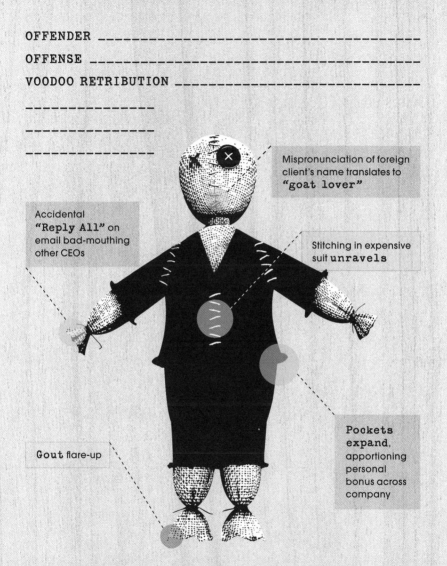

Mispronunciation of foreign client's name translates to **"goat lover"**

Accidental **"Reply All"** on email bad-mouthing other CEOs

Stitching in expensive suit **unravels**

Pockets expand, apportioning personal bonus across company

Gout flare-up

*** Check all that apply. Fill in your own spells and incantations. ***

35

YOUR HEXES _____
_____
_____

MORE CURSES _____
_____
_____
_____

Rate of **stress-related graying** increases exponentially

Toilet paper **stuck to heel**

OFFENDER _____

OFFENSE _____

VOODOO RETRIBUTION _____

_____

_____

_____

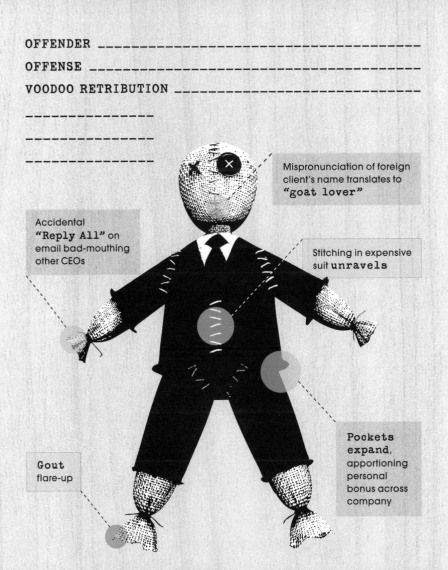

Mispronunciation of foreign client's name translates to **"goat lover"**

Accidental **"Reply All"** on email bad-mouthing other CEOs

Stitching in expensive suit **unravels**

Pockets expand, apportioning personal bonus across company

Gout flare-up

*** Check all that apply. Fill in your own spells and incantations. ***

YOUR HEXES _____

_____

_____

MORE CURSES _____

_____

_____

_____

Rate of **stress-related baldness** increases exponentially

Toilet paper **stuck to heel**

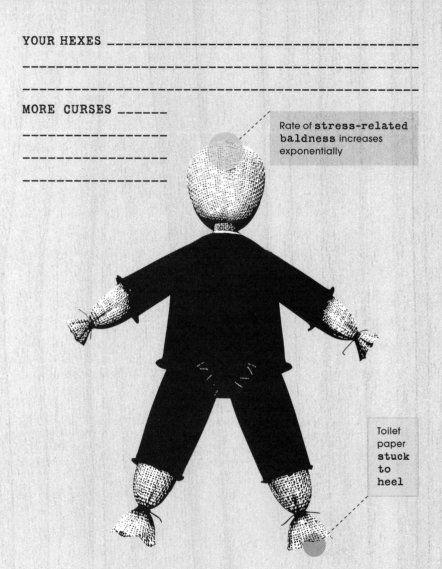

OFFENDER _____

OFFENSE _____

VOODOO RETRIBUTION _____

_____

_____

_____

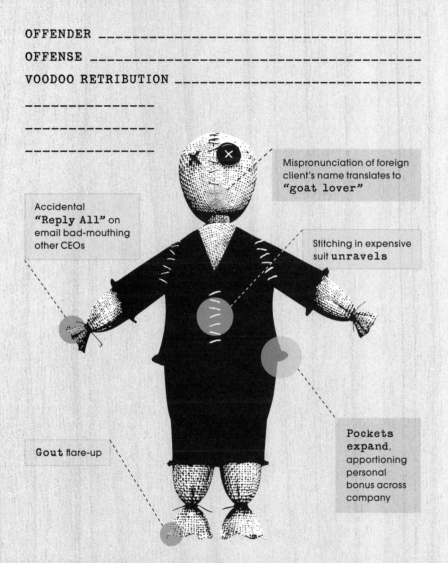

Mispronunciation of foreign client's name translates to **"goat lover"**

Accidental **"Reply All"** on email bad-mouthing other CEOs

Stitching in expensive suit **unravels**

Pockets expand, apportioning personal bonus across company

Gout flare-up

*** Check all that apply. Fill in your own spells and incantations. ***

39

Rate of **stress-related graying** increases exponentially

MORE CURSES

Toilet paper **stuck to heel**

OFFENDER _____

OFFENSE _____

VOODOO RETRIBUTION _____

_____

_____

_____

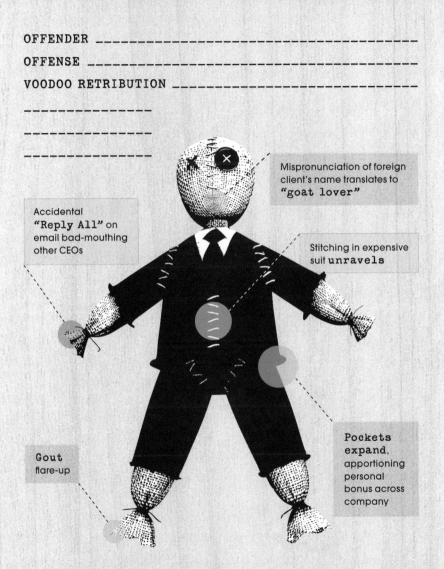

Mispronunciation of foreign
client's name translates to
"goat lover"

Accidental
"Reply All" on
email bad-mouthing
other CEOs

Stitching in expensive
suit **unravels**

**Pockets
expand,** apportioning
personal
bonus across
company

Gout
flare-up

*** Check all that apply. Fill in your own spells and incantations. ***

41

YOUR HEXES _____

_____

_____

MORE CURSES _ _ _ _ _ _

_ _ _ _ _ _ _ _ _ _ _ _ _ _ _ _

_ _ _ _ _ _ _ _ _ _ _ _ _ _ _ _

_ _ _ _ _ _ _ _ _ _ _ _ _ _ _ _

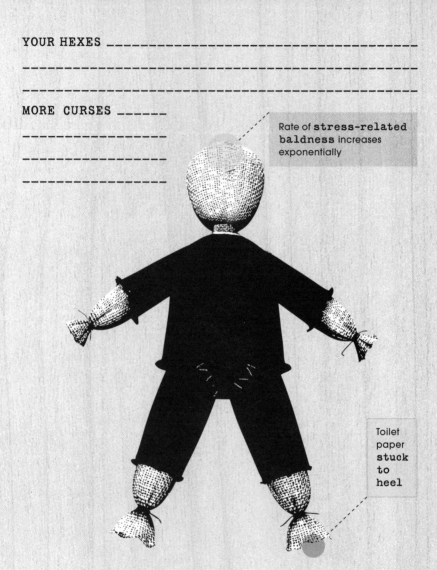

Rate of **stress-related baldness** increases exponentially

Toilet paper **stuck to heel**

OFFENDER _____

OFFENSE _____

VOODOO RETRIBUTION _____

_____

_____

_____

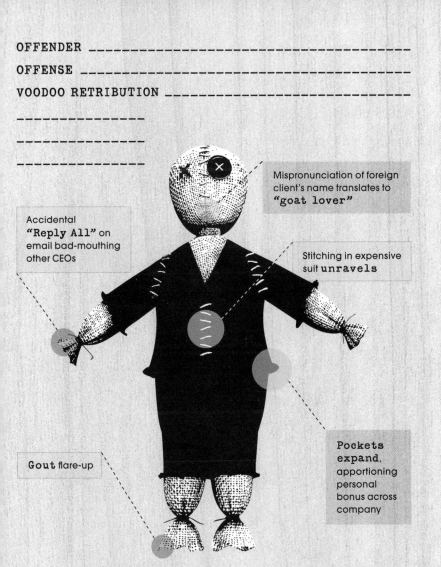

Mispronunciation of foreign client's name translates to **"goat lover"**

Accidental **"Reply All"** on email bad-mouthing other CEOs

Stitching in expensive suit **unravels**

Pockets expand, apportioning personal bonus across company

Gout flare-up

*** Check all that apply. Fill in your own spells and incantations. ***

YOUR HEXES _____
_____
_____

MORE CURSES _____
_____
_____
_____

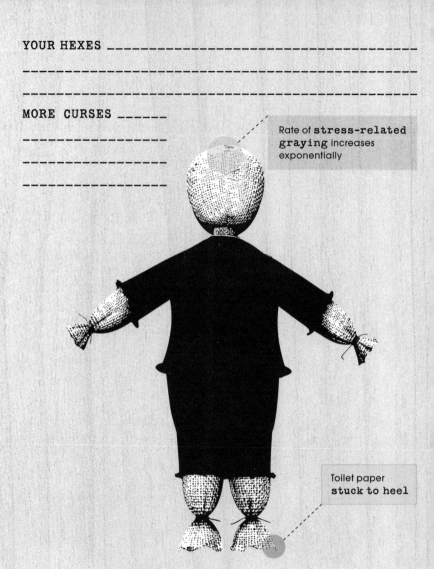

Rate of **stress-related graying** increases exponentially

Toilet paper **stuck to heel**

OFFENDER _____

OFFENSE _____

VOODOO RETRIBUTION _____

_____

_____

_____

Mispronunciation of foreign client's name translates to **"goat lover"**

Accidental **"Reply All"** on email bad-mouthing other CEOs

Stitching in expensive suit **unravels**

Pockets expand, apportioning personal bonus across company

Gout flare-up

*** Check all that apply. Fill in your own spells and incantations. ***

YOUR HEXES _____
_____
_____

MORE CURSES _____
_____
_____
_____

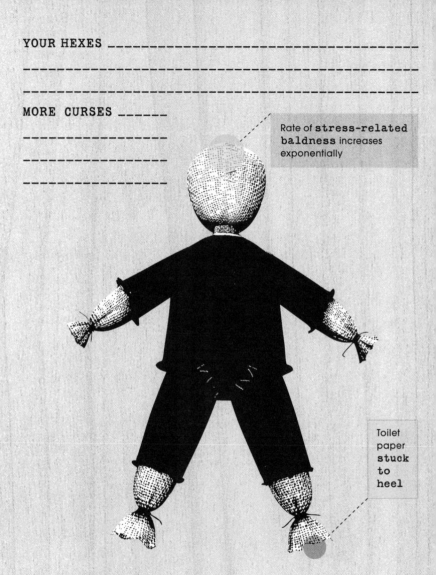

Rate of **stress-related baldness** increases exponentially

Toilet paper **stuck to heel**

OFFENDER _____

OFFENSE _____

VOODOO RETRIBUTION _____

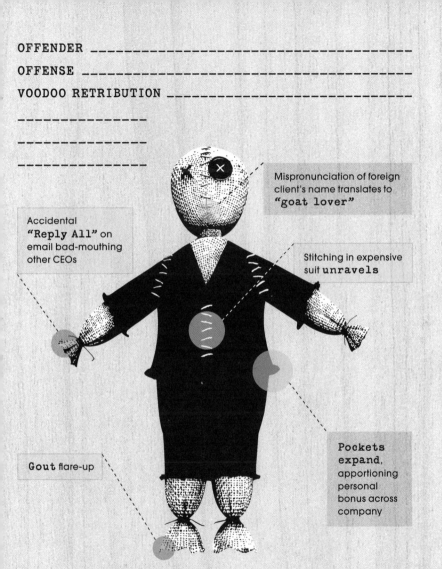

Mispronunciation of foreign client's name translates to **"goat lover"**

Accidental **"Reply All"** on email bad-mouthing other CEOs

Stitching in expensive suit **unravels**

Gout flare-up

Pockets expand, apportioning personal bonus across company

*** Check all that apply. Fill in your own spells and incantations. ***

MORE CURSES _____
_____
_____
_____

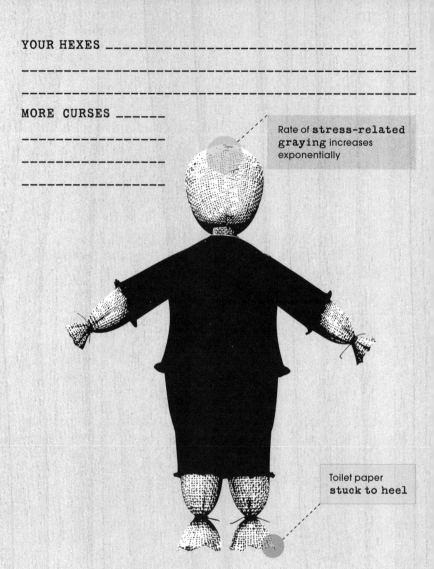

Rate of **stress-related graying** increases exponentially

Toilet paper **stuck to heel**

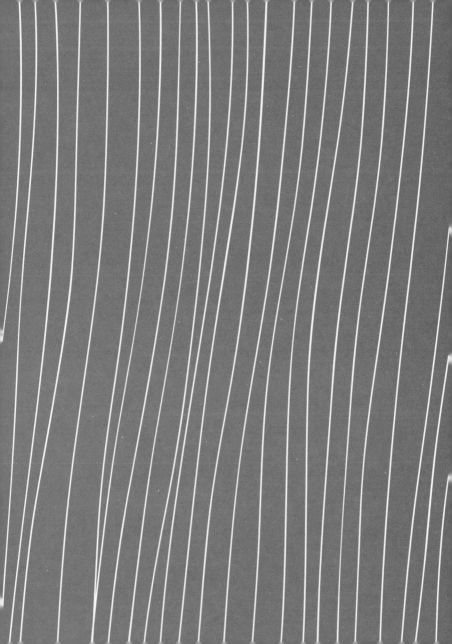

LUNCH THIEF

Lunch: the one small, shining oasis in a day otherwise full of mind-numbing drudgery.

Each second that ticks by in the morning is a countdown to lunch. You can picture your favorite food sitting in the fridge, clearly labeled with your name, waiting for you, calling to you. And then the time finally comes, but all you see is an empty spot where your lunch used to be.

M#*$^@! F*@#er!!!

You thought you lived in a civilized society. You thought people had a sense of decency and ownership. You were wrong! Some cheap a-hole didn't even bother to bring their own lunch because they figured, hey, why not just pick the choicest lunch out of the fridge, saving both time and money? Never you mind the absolute fiery rage it induces in others. Never mind that you now have to suffer through cafeteria food. Well, now you have something they didn't count on: *Office Voodoo*! Smote that SOB with a full-body coffee stain, or freeze their jaw open mid-bite. Make people reconsider the old adage, "two wrongs don't make a right."

OFFENDER _____

OFFENSE _____

VOODOO RETRIBUTION _____

Lockjaw freezes
mouth open

Unbelievably large,
**unsightly
coffee stain**

_____

_____

_____

**Thunder
thighs,** caused
by constant eating,
hinder upward
mobility on
corporate ladder

All stolen food
causes intense,
**Willy-Wonka-
style
bloating**

*** Check all that apply. Fill in your own spells and incantations. ***

MORE CURSES _ _ _ _
_ _ _ _ _ _ _ _ _ _ _ _ _ _
_ _ _ _ _ _ _ _ _ _ _ _ _ _
_ _ _ _ _ _ _ _ _ _ _ _ _ _
_ _ _ _ _ _ _ _ _ _ _ _ _ _

Entire meeting smells it and
knows who dealt it

OFFENDER _____

OFFENSE _____

VOODOO RETRIBUTION _____

Lockjaw freezes
mouth open

_____

_____

_____

Unbelievably large,
**unsightly
coffee stain**

**Thunder
thighs,** caused
by constant eating,
hinder upward
mobility on
corporate ladder

All stolen food
causes intense,
**Willy-Wonka-
style
bloating**

*** Check all that apply. Fill in your own spells and incantations. ***

53

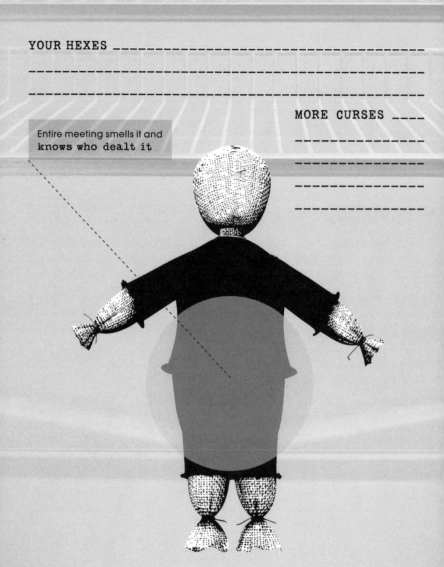

YOUR HEXES _____
_____
_____

MORE CURSES ____
_____
_____
_____
_____

Entire meeting smells it and
knows who dealt it

OFFENDER _____

OFFENSE _____

VOODOO RETRIBUTION _____

Lockjaw freezes
mouth open

_____
_____
_____

Unbelievably large,
**unsightly
coffee stain**

**Thunder
thighs,** caused
by constant eating,
hinder upward
mobility on
corporate ladder

All stolen food
causes intense,
**Willy-Wonka-
style
bloating**

*** Check all that apply. Fill in your own spells and incantations. ***

55

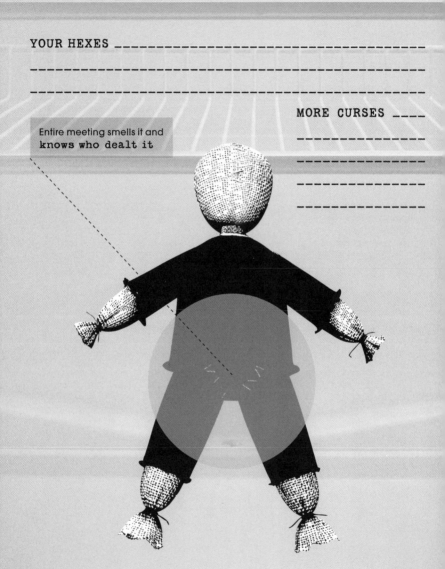

YOUR HEXES _____
_____
_____

MORE CURSES _____
_____
_____
_____
_____

Entire meeting smells it and
knows who dealt it

OFFENDER _____

OFFENSE _____

VOODOO RETRIBUTION _____

Lockjaw freezes mouth open

_____
_____
_____

Unbelievably large, **unsightly coffee stain**

Thunder thighs, caused by constant eating, hinder upward mobility on corporate ladder

All stolen food causes intense, **Willy-Wonka-style bloating**

*** Check all that apply. Fill in your own spells and incantations. ***

YOUR HEXES _____

_____

_____

MORE CURSES _____

_____

_____

_____

_____

Entire meeting smells it and
knows who dealt it

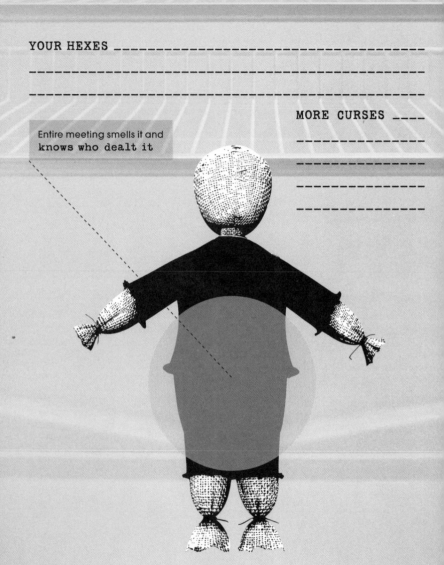

OFFENDER _____

OFFENSE _____

VOODOO RETRIBUTION _____

Lockjaw freezes
mouth open

Unbelievably large,
**unsightly
coffee stain**

_____

_____

_____

**Thunder
thighs,** caused
by constant eating,
hinder upward
mobility on
corporate ladder

All stolen food
causes intense,
**Willy-Wonka-
style
bloating**

*** Check all that apply. Fill in your own spells and incantations. ***

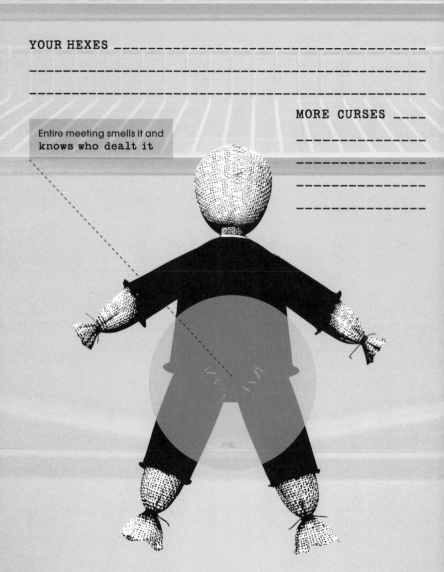

YOUR HEXES _____
_____
_____

MORE CURSES _____
_____
_____
_____
_____

Entire meeting smells it and
knows who dealt it

OFFENDER _____

OFFENSE _____

VOODOO RETRIBUTION _____

Lockjaw freezes
mouth open

_____

_____

_____

Unbelievably large,
**unsightly
coffee stain**

**Thunder
thighs,** caused
by constant eating,
hinder upward
mobility on
corporate ladder

All stolen food
causes intense,
**Willy-Wonka-
style
bloating**

*** Check all that apply. Fill in your own spells and incantations. ***

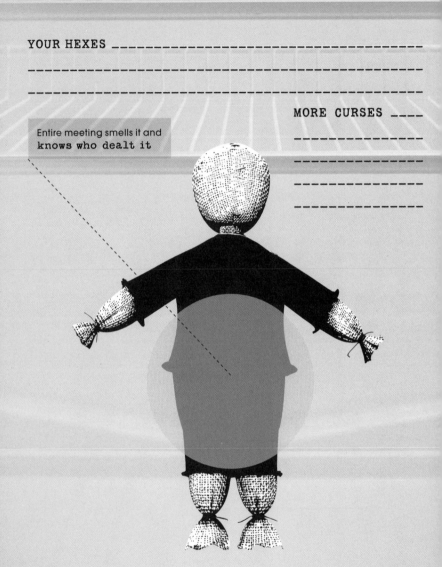

YOUR HEXES _____
_____
_____

MORE CURSES ____
_____
_____
_____
_____

Entire meeting smells it and
knows who dealt it

OFFENDER _____

OFFENSE _____

VOODOO RETRIBUTION _____

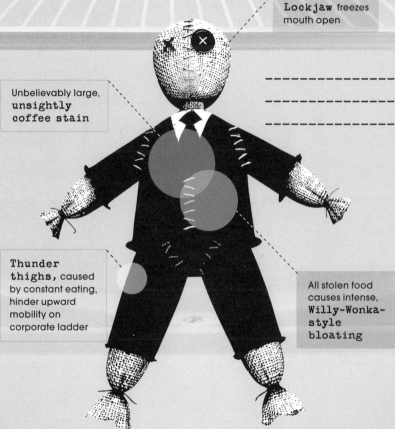

Lockjaw freezes mouth open

_____

_____

_____

Unbelievably large, **unsightly coffee stain**

Thunder thighs, caused by constant eating, hinder upward mobility on corporate ladder

All stolen food causes intense, **Willy-Wonka-style bloating**

*** Check all that apply. Fill in your own spells and incantations. ***

YOUR HEXES _____
_____
_____

MORE CURSES ____
_____
_____
_____
_____

Entire meeting smells it and
knows who dealt it

OFFENDER _____

OFFENSE _____

VOODOO RETRIBUTION _____

Lockjaw freezes mouth open

_____

_____

_____

Unbelievably large, **unsightly coffee stain**

Thunder thighs, caused by constant eating, hinder upward mobility on corporate ladder

All stolen food causes intense, **Willy-Wonka-style bloating**

*** Check all that apply. Fill in your own spells and incantations. ***

YOUR HEXES _____
_____
_____

MORE CURSES ____
_____
_____
_____
_____

Entire meeting smells it and
knows who dealt it

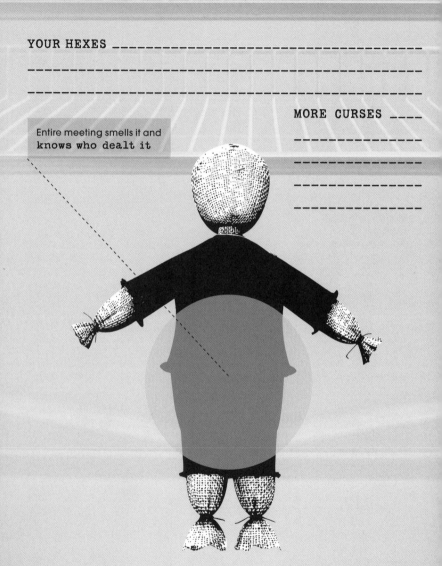

LOUD-TALKER

It's 9 a.m., you haven't had your coffee and maybe you're a little hungover.

Who can blame you when you know that you have to go to work everyday for the rest of your natural life and possibly beyond? All you probably want is a little peace and quiet to read through the fifty some odd company mandates you received in the blessed few hours between when you left last night and came in this morning. But can you get that little bit of solace? Not with the Loud-Talker down the hall. Oh, no. From the moment you stepped off the elevator you could hear that belly laugh rolling down the corridors, shaking the walls of the cubes. What the hell do they even have to laugh about? What's so important that they need to bellow it across the floor? Little Jimmy got a whole broccoli stalk stuck in his braces. BFD! The monthly report is behind schedule. Who cares? Not you. Not at 9 a.m. Now, with a little divine intervention, you don't have to hear about it. Just inflict a little laryngitis or conjure up a debilitating tongue cramp. Anything to shut that loud jerk up!

OFFENDER _____

OFFENSE _____

VOODOO RETRIBUTION _____

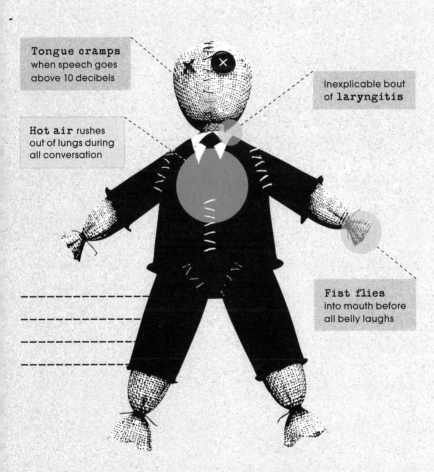

Tongue cramps when speech goes above 10 decibels

Inexplicable bout of **laryngitis**

Hot air rushes out of lungs during all conversation

Fist flies into mouth before all belly laughs

_____

_____

_____

_____

*** Check all that apply. Fill in your own spells and incantations. ***

YOUR HEXES _____

_____

_____

MORE CURSES _____

_____

_____

_____

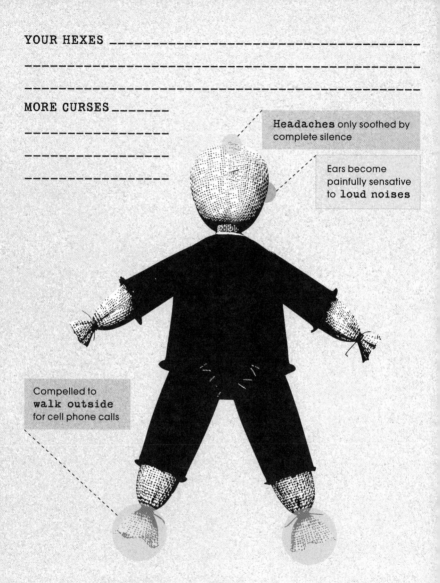

Headaches only soothed by complete silence

Ears become painfully sensative to loud noises

Compelled to walk outside for cell phone calls

OFFENDER _____

OFFENSE _____

VOODOO RETRIBUTION _____

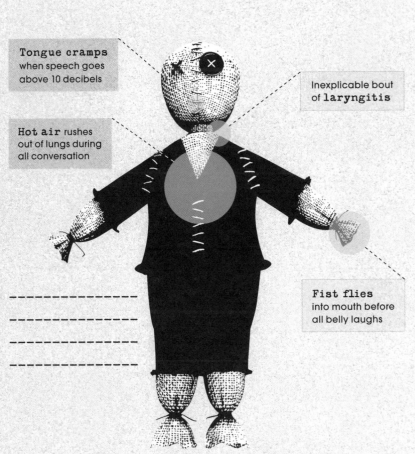

Tongue cramps when speech goes above 10 decibels

Inexplicable bout of **laryngitis**

Hot air rushes out of lungs during all conversation

Fist flies into mouth before all belly laughs

_____

_____

_____

_____

*** Check all that apply. Fill in your own spells and incantations. ***

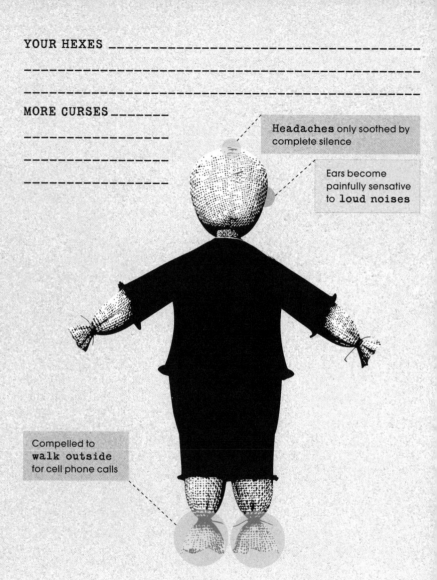

YOUR HEXES _____

_____

_____

MORE CURSES _____

_____

_____

_____

Headaches only soothed by complete silence

Ears become painfully sensative to loud noises

Compelled to walk outside for cell phone calls

OFFENDER _____

OFFENSE _____

VOODOO RETRIBUTION _____

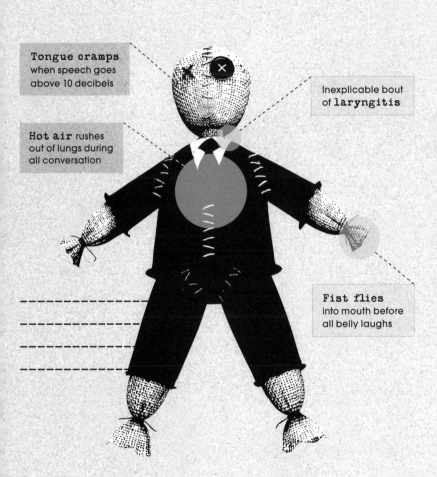

Tongue cramps when speech goes above 10 decibels

Inexplicable bout of **laryngitis**

Hot air rushes out of lungs during all conversation

Fist flies into mouth before all belly laughs

_____
_____
_____
_____

*** Check all that apply. Fill in your own spells and incantations. ***

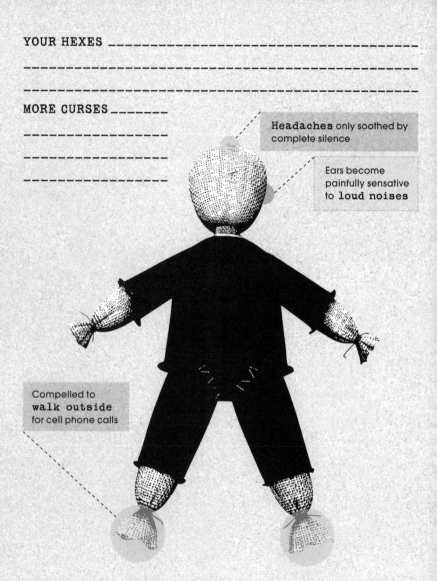

YOUR HEXES _____
_____
_____

MORE CURSES _____
_____
_____
_____

Headaches only soothed by complete silence

Ears become painfully sensative to loud noises

Compelled to walk outside for cell phone calls

OFFENDER _____

OFFENSE _____

VOODOO RETRIBUTION _____

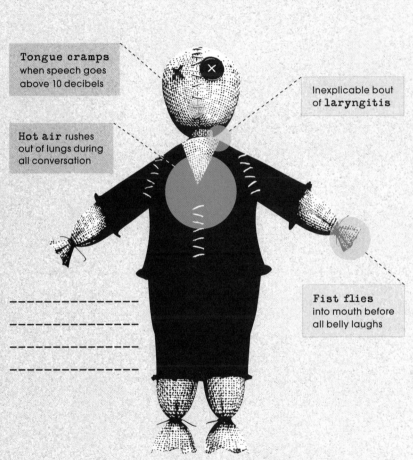

Tongue cramps when speech goes above 10 decibels

Inexplicable bout of **laryngitis**

Hot air rushes out of lungs during all conversation

Fist flies into mouth before all belly laughs

_____

_____

_____

_____

*** Check all that apply. Fill in your own spells and incantations. ***

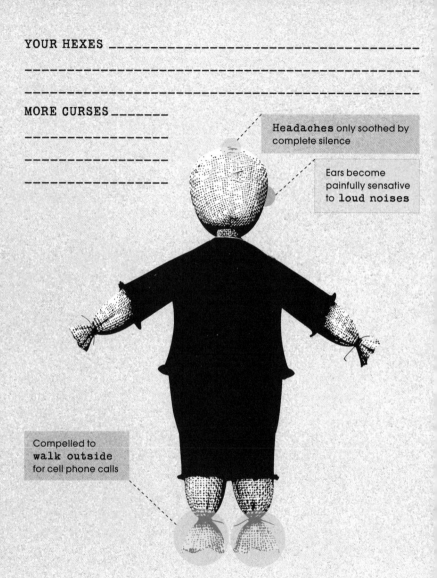

YOUR HEXES _____

_____

_____

MORE CURSES _____

_____

_____

_____

Headaches only soothed by complete silence

Ears become painfully sensative to **loud noises**

Compelled to **walk outside** for cell phone calls

OFFENDER _____

OFFENSE _____

VOODOO RETRIBUTION _____

Tongue cramps when speech goes above 10 decibels

Hot air rushes out of lungs during all conversation

Inexplicable bout of **laryngitis**

Fist flies into mouth before all belly laughs

_____

_____

_____

_____

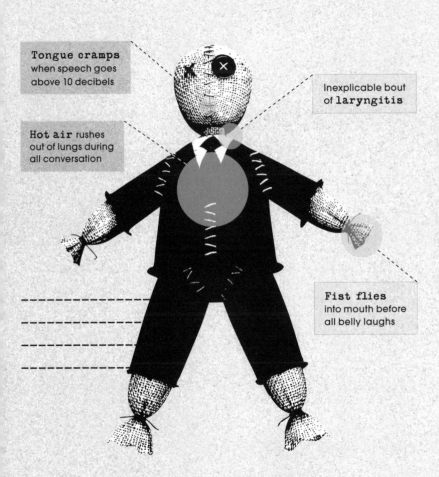

*** Check all that apply. Fill in your own spells and incantations. ***

77

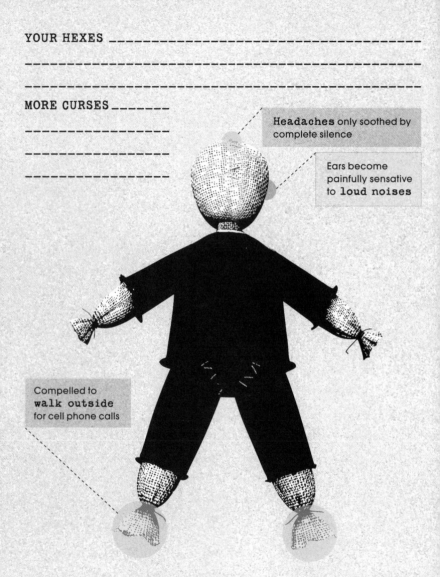

YOUR HEXES _____
_____
_____

MORE CURSES _____
_____
_____
_____

Headaches only soothed by complete silence

Ears become painfully sensative to loud noises

Compelled to walk outside for cell phone calls

OFFENDER _____

OFFENSE _____

VOODOO RETRIBUTION _____

Tongue cramps when speech goes above 10 decibels

Inexplicable bout of **laryngitis**

Hot air rushes out of lungs during all conversation

_____

_____

_____

_____

Fist flies into mouth before all belly laughs

*** Check all that apply. Fill in your own spells and incantations. ***

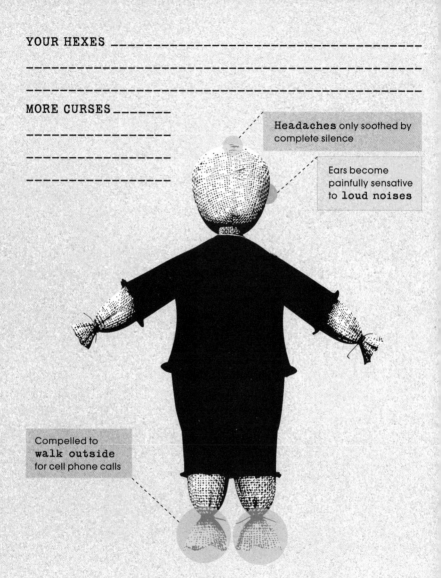

YOUR HEXES _____

_____

_____

MORE CURSES _____
_____

_____

_____

Headaches only soothed by complete silence

Ears become painfully sensative to loud noises

Compelled to walk outside for cell phone calls

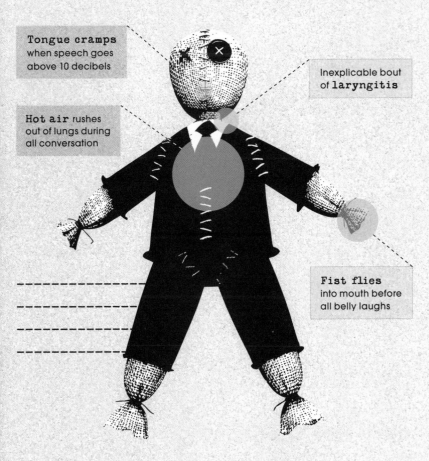

Tongue cramps when speech goes above 10 decibels

Hot air rushes out of lungs during all conversation

Inexplicable bout of **laryngitis**

Fist flies into mouth before all belly laughs

_____

_____

_____

_____

*** Check all that apply. Fill in your own spells and incantations. ***

YOUR HEXES _____

_____

_____

MORE CURSES _____

_____

_____

_____

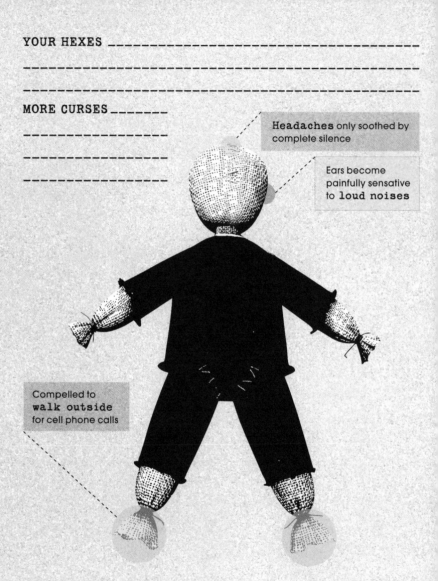

Headaches only soothed by complete silence

Ears become painfully sensative to **loud noises**

Compelled to **walk outside** for cell phone calls

OFFENDER _____

OFFENSE _____

VOODOO RETRIBUTION _____

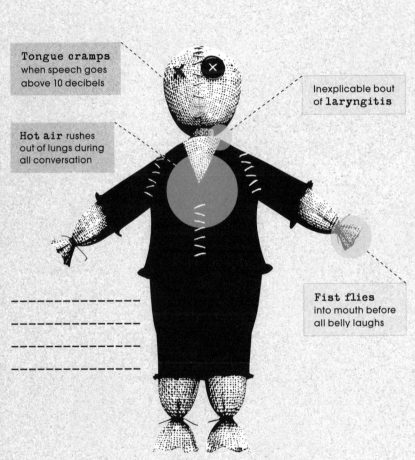

Tongue cramps
when speech goes
above 10 decibels

Inexplicable bout
of **laryngitis**

Hot air rushes
out of lungs during
all conversation

Fist flies
into mouth before
all belly laughs

_____

_____

_____

_____

*** Check all that apply. Fill in your own spells and incantations. ***

YOUR HEXES _____

_____

_____

MORE CURSES_____

_____

_____

_____

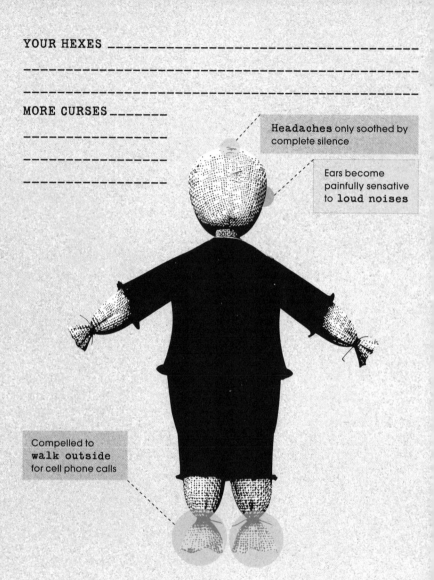

Headaches only soothed by complete silence

Ears become painfully sensitive to loud noises

Compelled to walk outside for cell phone calls

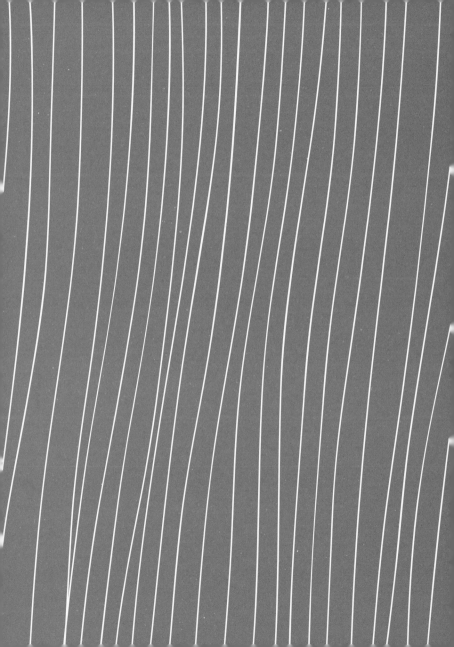

CREDIT-TAKER

You worked your ass off to finish on time—staying late, working through lunch, and pushing yourself to the absolute limits. Now you're done and you did an awesome job.

Then along comes Credit-Taker, sidling up next to you to steal your glory even though the only thing they did was ask you stupid questions that actually made the project take longer. But office etiquette dictates that you can't call someone out on the spot, or punch them in the side of the head, no matter how much they deserve it. At least now you can ensure that they will only attach their name to failing projects from here on out. Sure they'll get credit— credit for losing the company a pile of money on ridiculously ill-conceived ventures! But why stop there? Drop them from every cc list for projects they're actually working on (if any). Then, if you're so inclined, you can pick up the slack, pointing out that Credit-Taker must have had a bad month and problems at home, but you were happy to step in and lend a helping hand. After that incident with the stolen office supplies, it was the least you could do to help them get back on their feet.

OFFENDER _____

OFFENSE _____

VOODOO RETRIBUTION _____

Lips lock when words "I worked on it with..." begin to form

_____

_____

_____

Doomed to only attach name to **failing projects**

Name **disappears** from all cc lists

Caught red-handed with pilfered office supplies

Knees give out whenever following someone else's project

*** Check all that apply. Fill in your own spells and incantations. ***

87

YOUR HEXES _____

_____

_____

MORE CURSES _____

_____

_____

_____

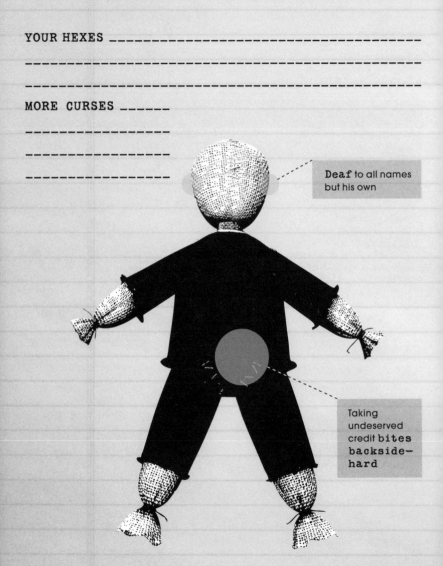

Deaf to all names but his own

Taking undeserved credit **bites backside— hard**

OFFENDER _____

OFFENSE _____

VOODOO RETRIBUTION _____

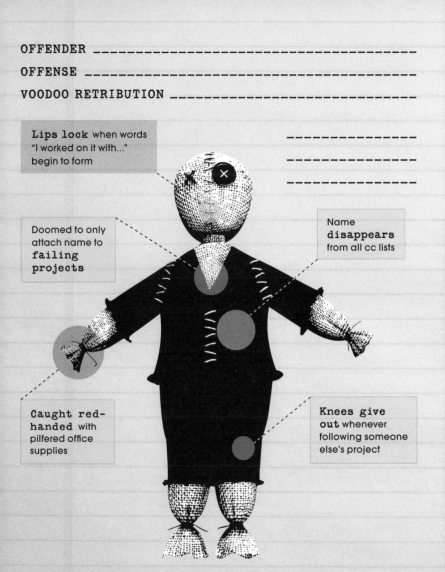

Lips lock when words "I worked on it with..." begin to form

_____

_____

_____

Doomed to only attach name to **failing projects**

Name **disappears** from all cc lists

Caught red-handed with pilfered office supplies

Knees give out whenever following someone else's project

*** Check all that apply. Fill in your own spells and incantations. ***

YOUR HEXES _____

_____

_____

MORE CURSES _____

_____

_____

_____

Deaf to all names
but her own

Taking
undeserved
credit **bites
backside—
hard**

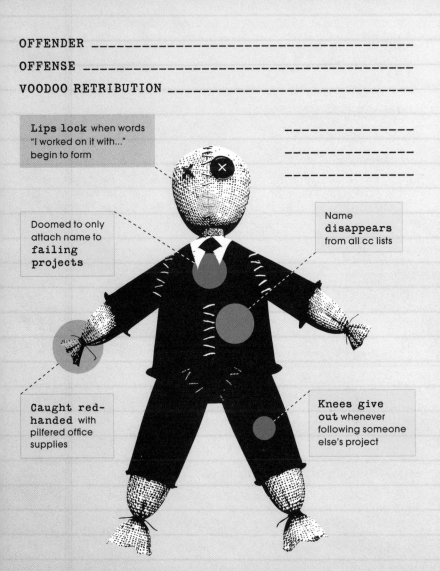

OFFENDER _____

OFFENSE _____

VOODOO RETRIBUTION _____

_____
_____
_____

Lips lock when words "I worked on it with..." begin to form

Doomed to only attach name to **failing projects**

Name **disappears** from all cc lists

Caught red-handed with pilfered office supplies

Knees give out whenever following someone else's project

*** Check all that apply. Fill in your own spells and incantations. ***

91

MORE CURSES _____
_____
_____
_____

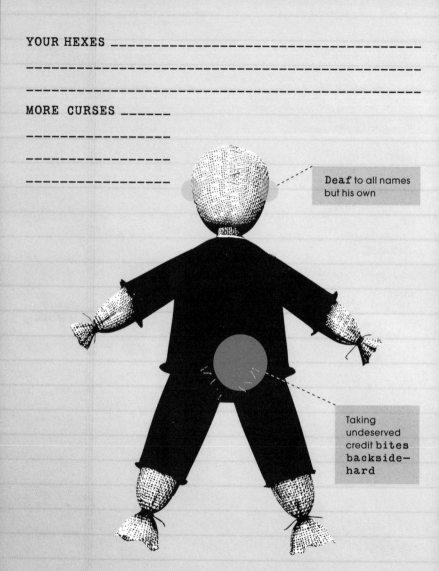

Deaf to all names but his own

Taking undeserved credit **bites backside— hard**

OFFENDER _____

OFFENSE _____

VOODOO RETRIBUTION _____

Lips lock when words
"I worked on it with..."
begin to form

_____

_____

_____

Doomed to only
attach name to
**failing
projects**

Name
disappears
from all cc lists

**Caught red-
handed** with
pilfered office
supplies

**Knees give
out** whenever
following someone
else's project

*** Check all that apply. Fill in your own spells and incantations. ***

YOUR HEXES _____
_____
_____

MORE CURSES _____

_____

_____

_____

Deaf to all names but her own

Taking undeserved credit **bites backside— hard**

OFFENDER _____

OFFENSE _____

VOODOO RETRIBUTION _____

Lips lock when words "I worked on it with..." begin to form

_____

_____

_____

Doomed to only attach name to **failing projects**

Name **disappears** from all cc lists

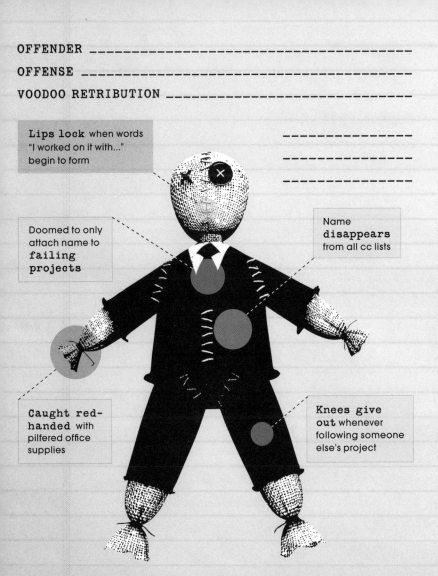

Caught red-handed with pilfered office supplies

Knees give out whenever following someone else's project

*** Check all that apply. Fill in your own spells and incantations. ***

YOUR HEXES _____

_____

_____

MORE CURSES _____

_____

_____

_____

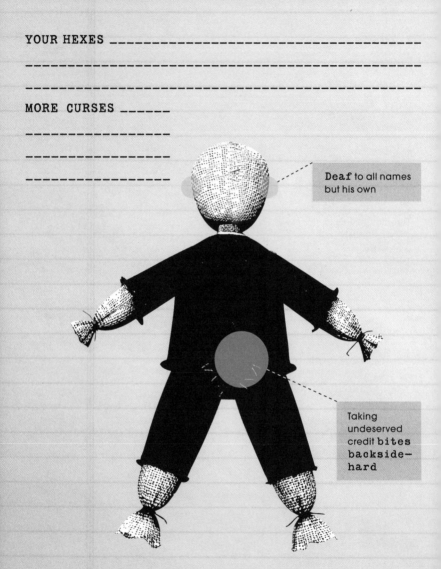

Deaf to all names
but his own

Taking
undeserved
credit bites
backside—
hard

OFFENDER _____

OFFENSE _____

VOODOO RETRIBUTION _____

Lips lock when words "I worked on it with..." begin to form

_____

_____

_____

Doomed to only attach name to **failing projects**

Name **disappears** from all cc lists

Caught red-handed with pilfered office supplies

Knees give out whenever following someone else's project

*** Check all that apply. Fill in your own spells and incantations. ***

97

YOUR HEXES _____
_____
_____

MORE CURSES _____
_____
_____
_____

Deaf to all names but her own

Taking undeserved credit bites backside-hard

OFFENDER _____

OFFENSE _____

VOODOO RETRIBUTION _____

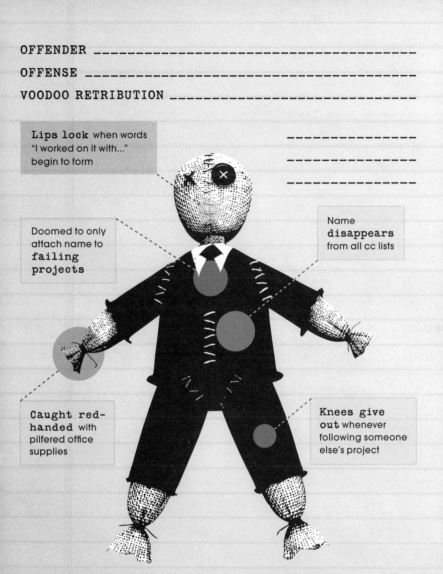

Lips lock when words "I worked on it with..." begin to form

_____
_____
_____

Doomed to only attach name to failing projects

Name **disappears** from all cc lists

Caught red-handed with pilfered office supplies

Knees give out whenever following someone else's project

*** Check all that apply. Fill in your own spells and incantations. ***

Deaf to all names
but his own

Taking
undeserved
credit bites
backside—
hard

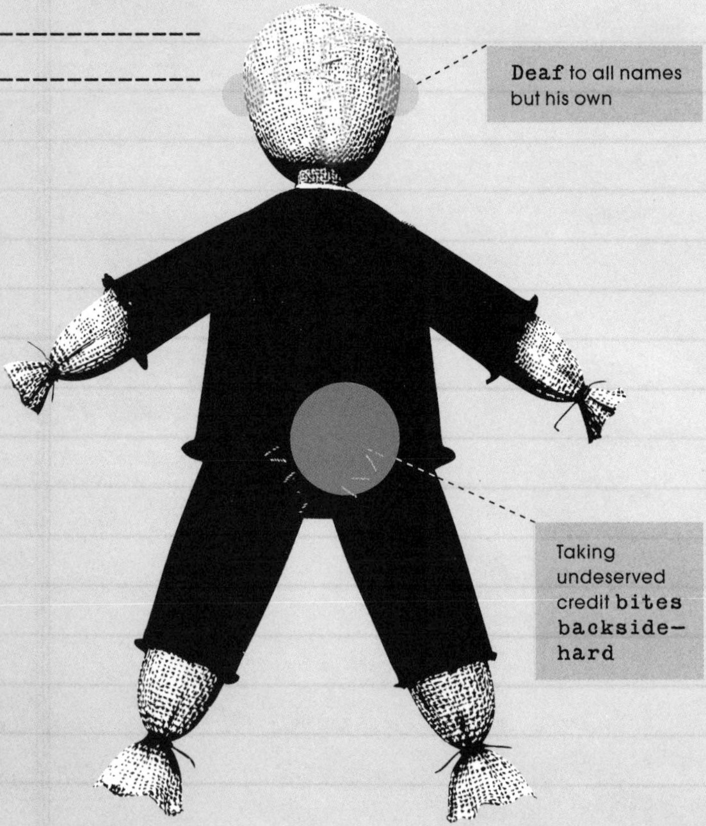

OFFENDER _____

OFFENSE _____

VOODOO RETRIBUTION _____

Lips lock when words
"I worked on it with..."
begin to form

_____

_____

_____

Doomed to only
attach name to
**failing
projects**

Name
disappears
from all cc lists

**Caught red-
handed** with
pilfered office
supplies

**Knees give
out** whenever
following someone
else's project

*** Check all that apply. Fill in your own spells and incantations. ***

101

YOUR HEXES _____
_____
_____

MORE CURSES _____
_____
_____
_____

Deaf to all names but her own

Taking undeserved credit **bites backside— hard**

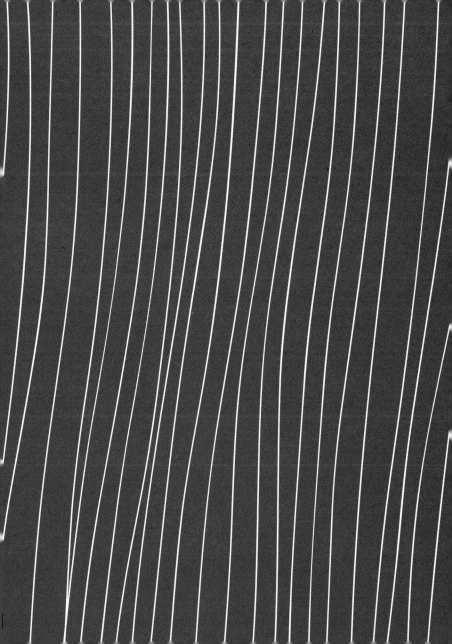

INANE SMALL-TALKER

Did you see what happened on *Lost* last night!? No? Then, oh my god, did you see who got ousted from some random reality TV show about families, fashion, cakes, pets, or whatever-the-hell else?

No, and you probably don't friggen care either. But that doesn't stop the Inane Small-Talker from asking you everyday if you watch whatever mindless, brain-eroding slop they watch. And even when you tell them you don't watch *The Real World, Season 83: Bangladesh*, they feel obliged to give you a complete recap accompanied by their own commentary, subsidized by what their mom thought of it. Then, if that wasn't exciting enough, they go on to tell you about every other detail of their life, from the color of their toothbrush—red and white—to the consistency of the carrots they ate with dinner last night—steamed a little too much so they were mushy like mashed potatoes when they should have been crisp like fresh asparagus. It's at that point that you probably blackout from banging your head on your desk. For your sanity, try a little incantation that cuts off their cable or a confounding charm that causes them to lose their way whenever they head to your desk. Your brain will thank you.

OFFENDER _____

OFFENSE _____

VOODOO RETRIBUTION _____

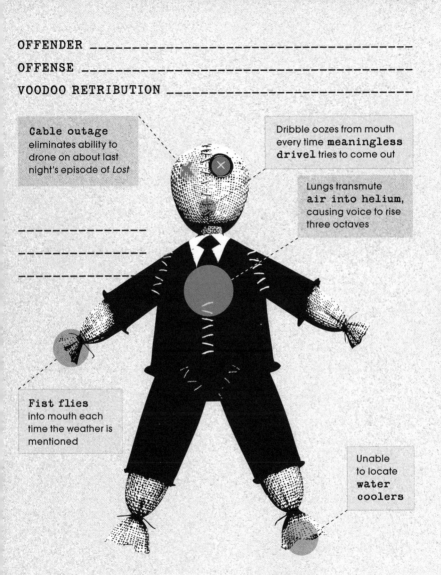

Cable outage
eliminates ability to
drone on about last
night's episode of *Lost*

Dribble oozes from mouth
every time **meaningless
drivel** tries to come out

Lungs transmute
air into helium,
causing voice to rise
three octaves

_____

_____

_____

Fist flies
into mouth each
time the weather is
mentioned

Unable
to locate
**water
coolers**

*** Check all that apply. Fill in your own spells and incantations. ***

YOUR HEXES _____
_____
_____

MORE CURSES _____
_____
_____
_____

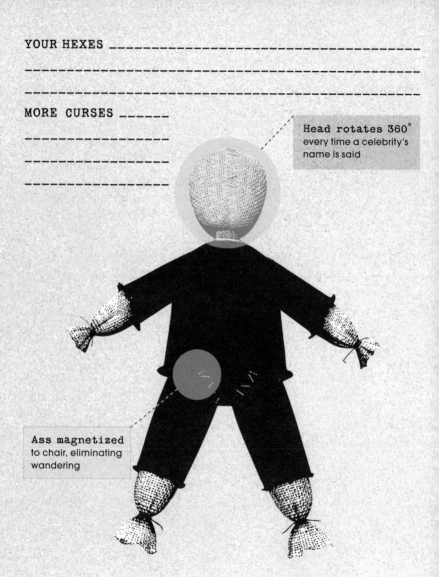

Head rotates 360°
every time a celebrity's
name is said

Ass magnetized
to chair, eliminating
wandering

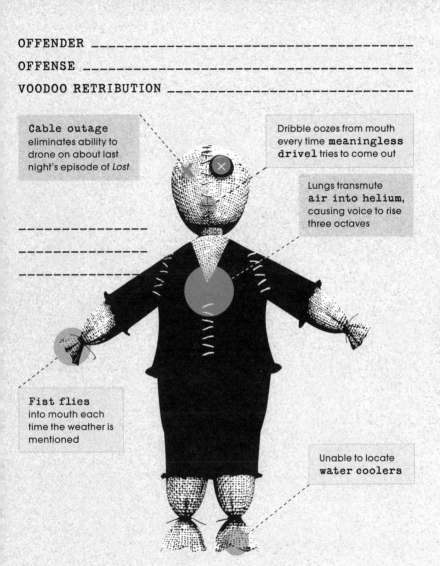

Cable outage
eliminates ability to
drone on about last
night's episode of *Lost*

Dribble oozes from mouth
every time **meaningless
drivel** tries to come out

Lungs transmute
air into helium,
causing voice to rise
three octaves

_____

_____

_____

Fist flies
into mouth each
time the weather is
mentioned

Unable to locate
water coolers

*** Check all that apply. Fill in your own spells and incantations. ***

YOUR HEXES _____

_____

_____

MORE CURSES _____

_____

_____

_____

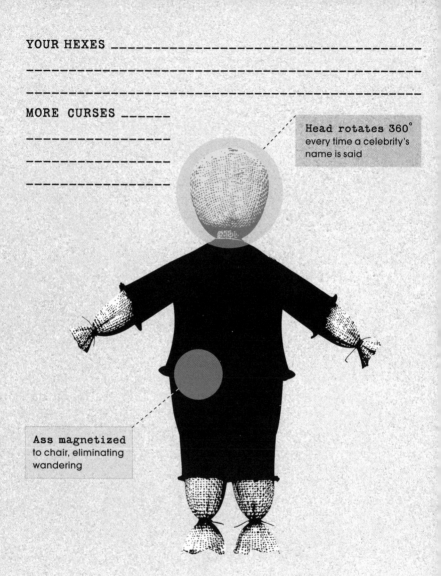

Head rotates 360° every time a celebrity's name is said

Ass magnetized to chair, eliminating wandering

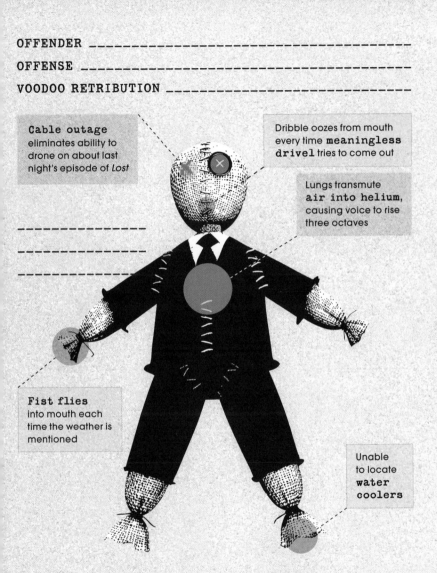

Cable outage eliminates ability to drone on about last night's episode of *Lost*

Dribble oozes from mouth every time **meaningless drivel** tries to come out

Lungs transmute **air into helium,** causing voice to rise three octaves

_____

_____

_____

Fist flies into mouth each time the weather is mentioned

Unable to locate **water coolers**

*** Check all that apply. Fill in your own spells and incantations. ***

109

YOUR HEXES _____

_____

_____

MORE CURSES _____

_____

_____

_____

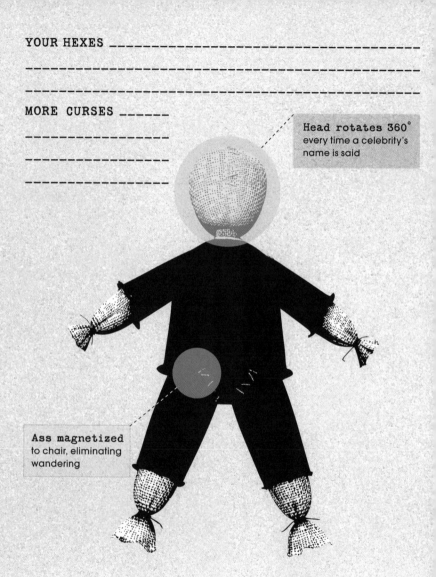

Head rotates 360° every time a celebrity's name is said

Ass magnetized to chair, eliminating wandering

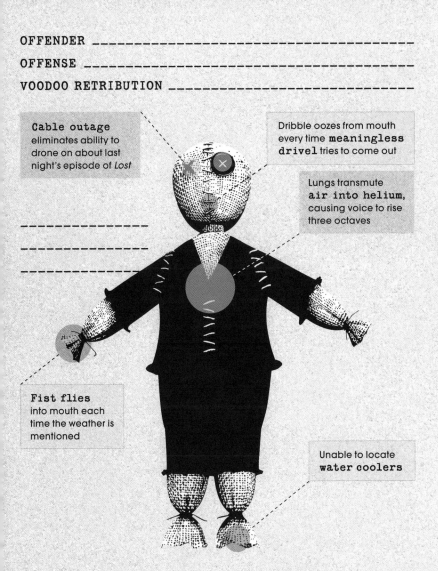

OFFENDER _____

OFFENSE _____

VOODOO RETRIBUTION _____

Cable outage eliminates ability to drone on about last night's episode of *Lost*

Dribble oozes from mouth every time **meaningless drivel** tries to come out

Lungs transmute **air into helium**, causing voice to rise three octaves

_____

_____

_____

Fist flies into mouth each time the weather is mentioned

Unable to locate **water coolers**

*** Check all that apply. Fill in your own spells and incantations. ***

YOUR HEXES _____

_____

_____

MORE CURSES _____

_____

_____

_____

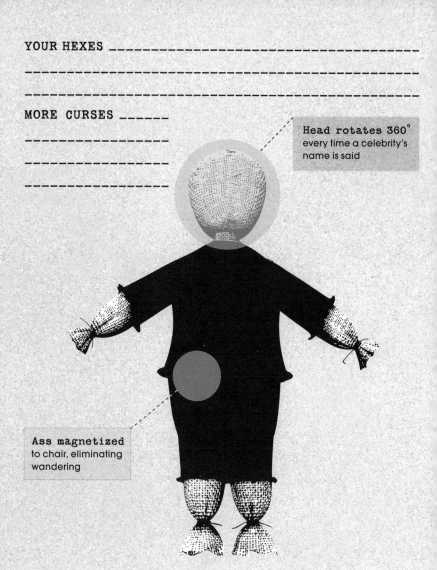

Head rotates 360° every time a celebrity's name is said

Ass magnetized to chair, eliminating wandering

OFFENDER _____

OFFENSE _____

VOODOO RETRIBUTION _____

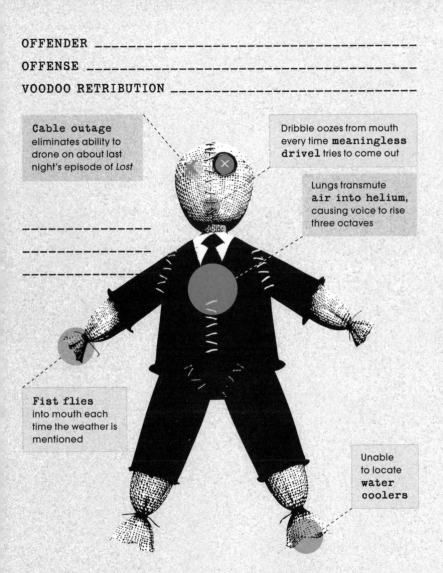

Cable outage eliminates ability to drone on about last night's episode of *Lost*

Dribble oozes from mouth every time **meaningless drivel** tries to come out

Lungs transmute **air into helium,** causing voice to rise three octaves

_____

_____

_____

Fist flies into mouth each time the weather is mentioned

Unable to locate **water coolers**

*** Check all that apply. Fill in your own spells and incantations. ***

MORE CURSES _____
_____
_____
_____

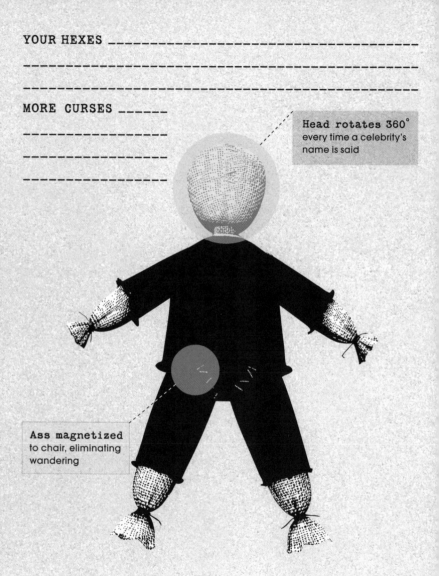

Head rotates 360°
every time a celebrity's
name is said

Ass magnetized
to chair, eliminating
wandering

OFFENDER _____

OFFENSE _____

VOODOO RETRIBUTION _____

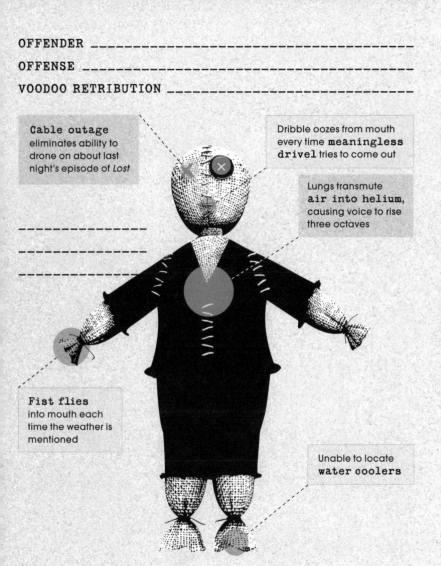

Cable outage
eliminates ability to
drone on about last
night's episode of *Lost*

Dribble oozes from mouth
every time **meaningless
drivel** tries to come out

Lungs transmute
air into helium,
causing voice to rise
three octaves

_____

_____

_____

Fist flies
into mouth each
time the weather is
mentioned

Unable to locate
water coolers

*** Check all that apply. Fill in your own spells and incantations. ***

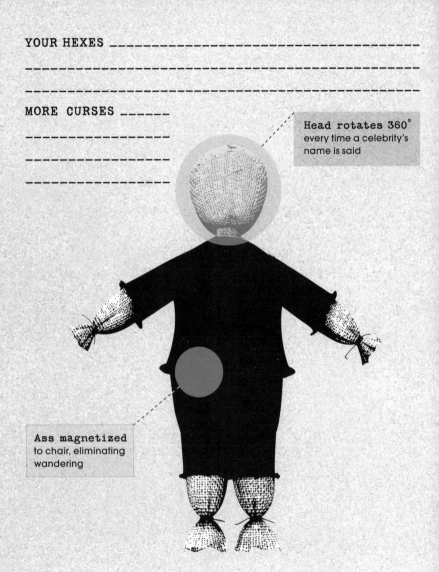

YOUR HEXES _____

_____

_____

MORE CURSES _____

_____

_____

_____

Head rotates 360°
every time a celebrity's
name is said

Ass magnetized
to chair, eliminating
wandering

OFFENDER _____

OFFENSE _____

VOODOO RETRIBUTION _____

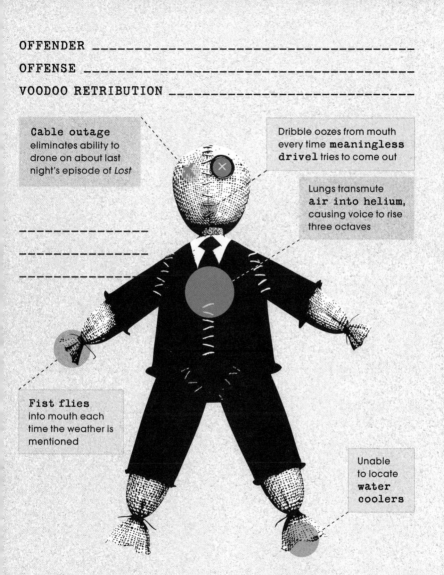

Cable outage
eliminates ability to
drone on about last
night's episode of *Lost*

Dribble oozes from mouth
every time **meaningless
drivel** tries to come out

Lungs transmute
air into helium,
causing voice to rise
three octaves

_____

_____

_____

Fist flies
into mouth each
time the weather is
mentioned

Unable
to locate
**water
coolers**

*** Check all that apply. Fill in your own spells and incantations. ***

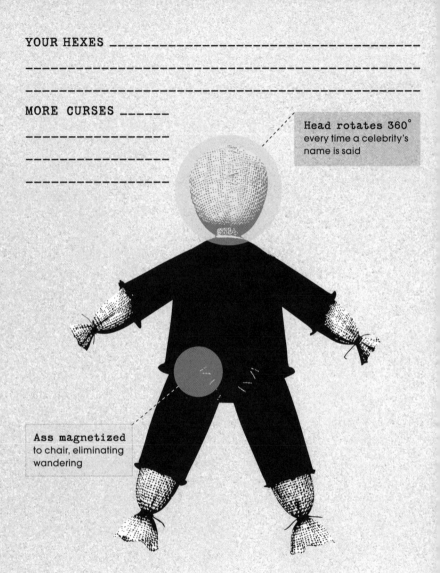

YOUR HEXES _____
_____
_____

MORE CURSES _____
_____
_____
_____

Head rotates 360° every time a celebrity's name is said

Ass magnetized to chair, eliminating wandering

OFFENDER _____

OFFENSE _____

VOODOO RETRIBUTION _____

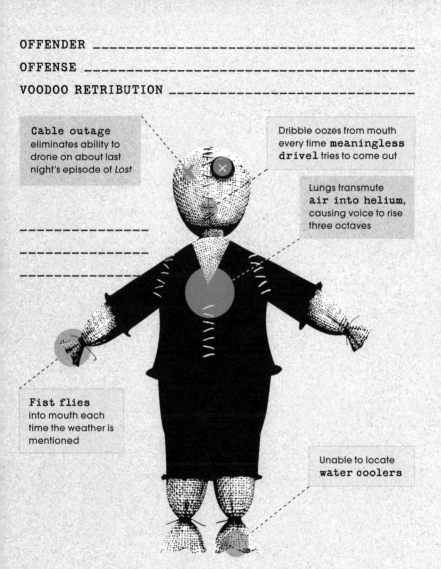

Cable outage eliminates ability to drone on about last night's episode of *Lost*

Dribble oozes from mouth every time **meaningless drivel** tries to come out

Lungs transmute **air into helium**, causing voice to rise three octaves

_____

_____

_____

Fist flies into mouth each time the weather is mentioned

Unable to locate **water coolers**

*** Check all that apply. Fill in your own spells and incantations. ***

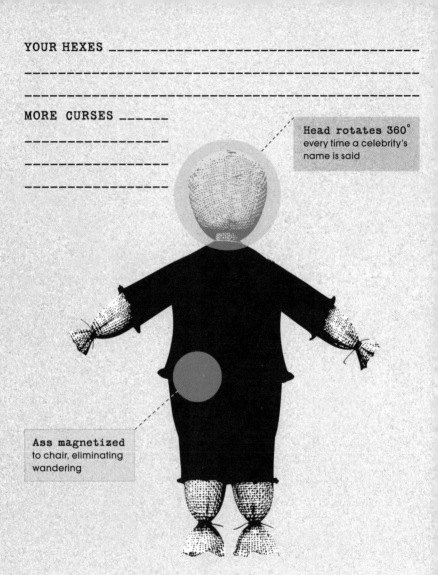

YOUR HEXES _____

_____

_____

MORE CURSES _____

_____

_____

_____

Head rotates 360° every time a celebrity's name is said

Ass magnetized to chair, eliminating wandering

120

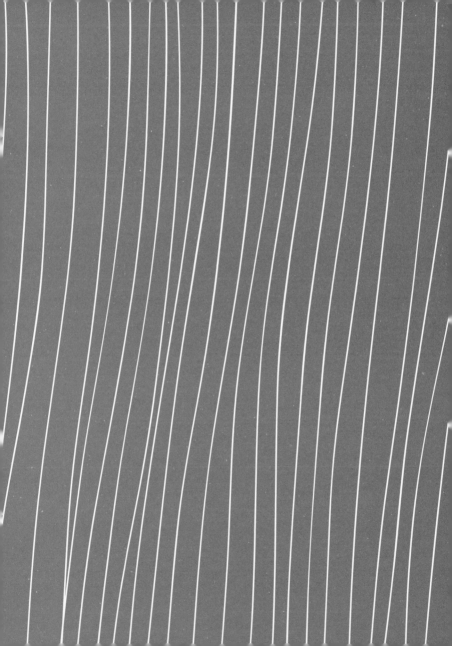

SENSELESS MEETING-SCHEDULER

It's Monday at 9:00 a.m., time for a meeting on the week's progress thus far. It's Wednesday at noon, time to go to a meeting—

where food will not be provided—to talk about the lack of support for the company's miniature golf league. It's Friday at 4:45 p.m., the perfect time for a meeting highlighting tips on effective ways to best utilize binder clips and Wite-Out. It's any time of any day, and you have to put down whatever you're doing to go and test your ability to stay awake while enduring a barrage of useless information that absolutely no one could possibly care about, except of course for the Senseless Meeting-Scheduler who thinks they look worth their bloated salary when they reserve the main conference room and get to hear themselves talk on and on and on and on about whatever topic they scrounged up that day. You don't want to go, but they're a dashed-line above of you on that ridiculous org chart that they went over in painfully explicit detail in a four-hour meeting last month. What they need is a mysterious case of amnesia for your existence so they can't include you on invites, or maybe it would be better for everyone if their datebook had a run-in with the shredder. It could happen—especially if you make it happen.

OFFENDER _____

OFFENSE _____

VOODOO RETRIBUTION _____

_____

_____

_____

_____

Mind blanks on your name, eliminating invitation to pointless meeting

Crushing workload makes scheduling senseless meetings impossible

Compelled to **bring snacks,** adding one redeeming quality to meetings

Datebook mystically leaps to own death in the **shredder** (or deletes itself if electronic)

*** Check all that apply. Fill in your own spells and incantations. ***

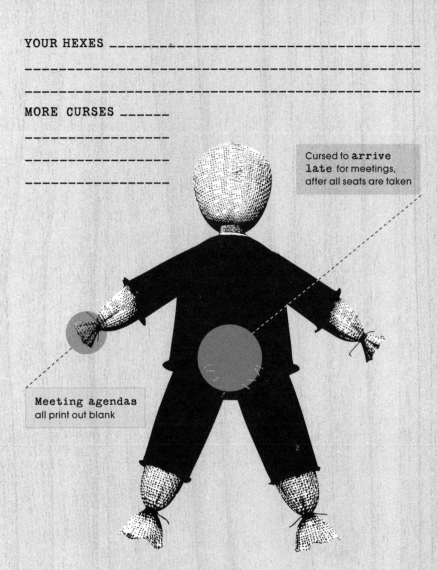

YOUR HEXES _____

MORE CURSES _____

_____

_____

_____

Cursed to **arrive late** for meetings, after all seats are taken

Meeting agendas all print out blank

OFFENDER _____

OFFENSE _____

VOODOO RETRIBUTION _____

_____

_____

_____

_____

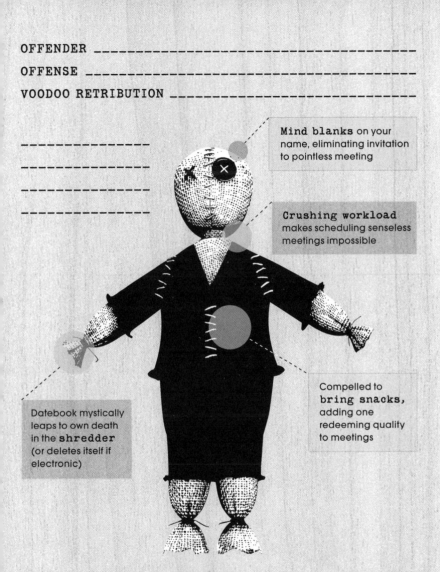

Mind blanks on your name, eliminating invitation to pointless meeting

Crushing workload makes scheduling senseless meetings impossible

Compelled to **bring snacks,** adding one redeeming quality to meetings

Datebook mystically leaps to own death in the **shredder** (or deletes itself if electronic)

*** Check all that apply. Fill in your own spells and incantations. ***

YOUR HEXES _____

_____

_____

MORE CURSES _____

_____

_____

_____

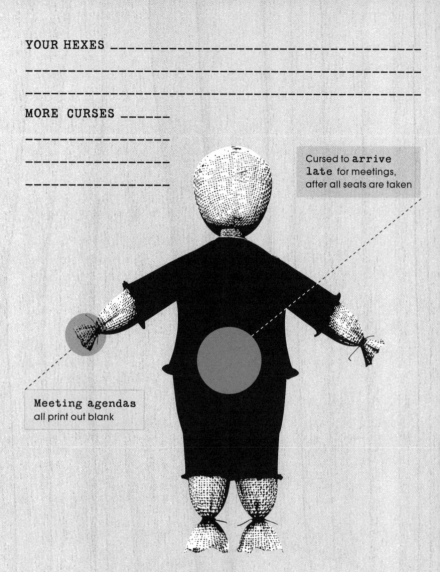

Cursed to **arrive late** for meetings, after all seats are taken

Meeting agendas
all print out blank

OFFENDER _____

OFFENSE _____

VOODOO RETRIBUTION _____

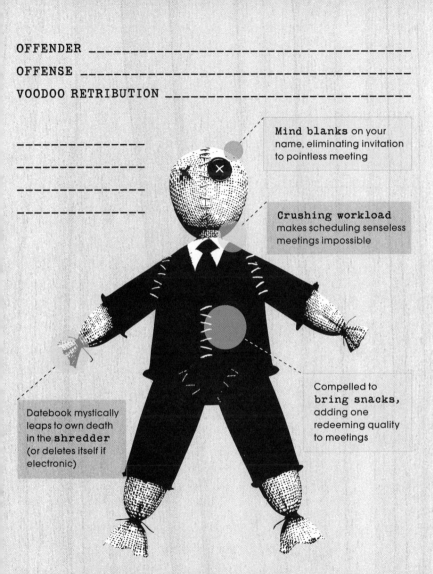

Mind blanks on your name, eliminating invitation to pointless meeting

Crushing workload makes scheduling senseless meetings impossible

Compelled to **bring snacks,** adding one redeeming quality to meetings

Datebook mystically leaps to own death in the **shredder** (or deletes itself if electronic)

*** Check all that apply. Fill in your own spells and incantations. ***

YOUR HEXES _____

_____

_____

MORE CURSES _____

_____

_____

_____

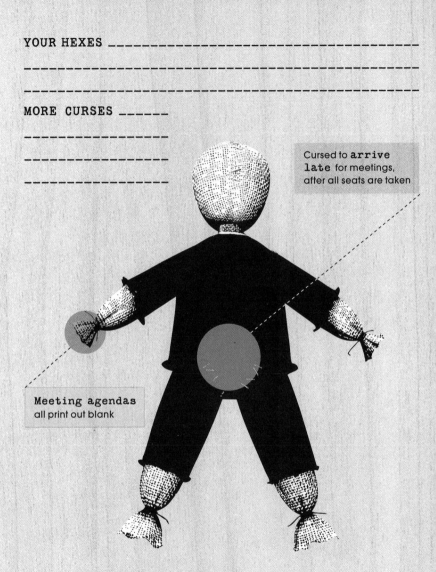

Cursed to **arrive late** for meetings, after all seats are taken

Meeting agendas all print out blank

OFFENDER _____

OFFENSE _____

VOODOO RETRIBUTION _____

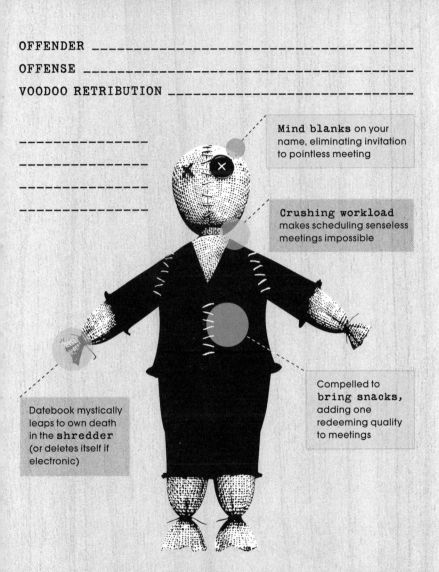

_____

_____

_____

_____

Mind blanks on your name, eliminating invitation to pointless meeting

Crushing workload makes scheduling senseless meetings impossible

Datebook mystically leaps to own death in the **shredder** (or deletes itself if electronic)

Compelled to **bring snacks,** adding one redeeming quality to meetings

*** Check all that apply. Fill in your own spells and incantations. ***

MORE CURSES _____

_____

_____

_____

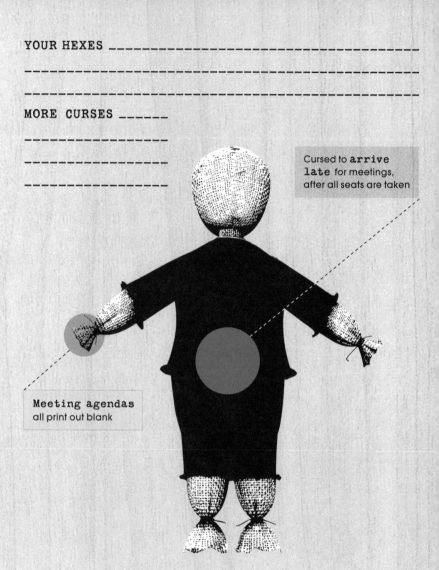

Cursed to **arrive late** for meetings, after all seats are taken

Meeting agendas all print out blank

OFFENDER _____

OFFENSE _____

VOODOO RETRIBUTION _____

_____

_____

_____

_____

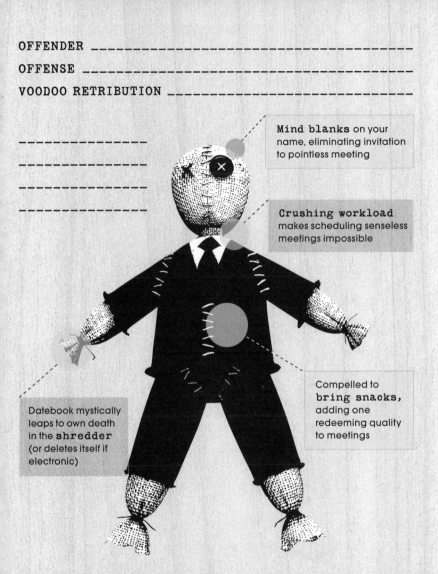

Mind blanks on your name, eliminating invitation to pointless meeting

Crushing workload makes scheduling senseless meetings impossible

Compelled to **bring snacks,** adding one redeeming quality to meetings

Datebook mystically leaps to own death in the **shredder** (or deletes itself if electronic)

*** Check all that apply. Fill in your own spells and incantations. ***

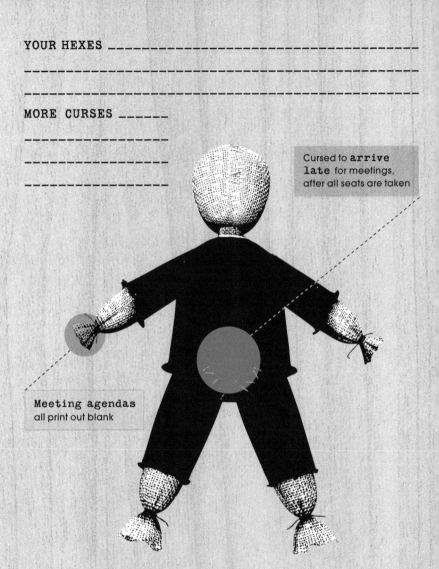

YOUR HEXES _____

_____

_____

MORE CURSES _____

_____

_____

_____

Cursed to **arrive late** for meetings, after all seats are taken

Meeting agendas all print out blank

OFFENDER _____

OFFENSE _____

VOODOO RETRIBUTION _____

_____

_____

_____

_____

Mind blanks on your name, eliminating invitation to pointless meeting

Crushing workload makes scheduling senseless meetings impossible

Compelled to **bring snacks,** adding one redeeming quality to meetings

Datebook mystically leaps to own death in the **shredder** (or deletes itself if electronic)

*** Check all that apply. Fill in your own spells and incantations. ***

MORE CURSES _____

_____

_____

_____

Cursed to **arrive late** for meetings, after all seats are taken

Meeting agendas all print out blank

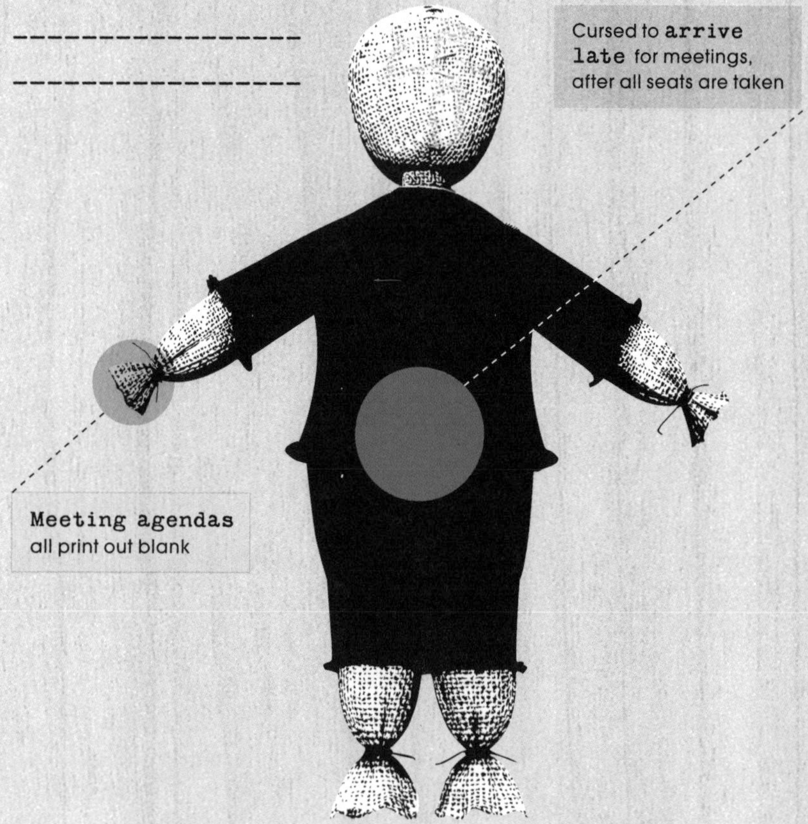

OFFENDER _____

OFFENSE _____

VOODOO RETRIBUTION _____

_____

_____

_____

_____

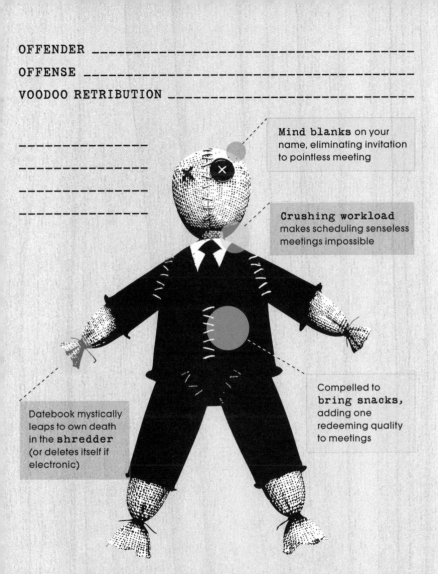

Mind blanks on your name, eliminating invitation to pointless meeting

Crushing workload makes scheduling senseless meetings impossible

Compelled to **bring snacks,** adding one redeeming quality to meetings

Datebook mystically leaps to own death in the **shredder** (or deletes itself if electronic)

*** Check all that apply. Fill in your own spells and incantations. ***

YOUR HEXES _____
_____
_____

MORE CURSES _____
_____
_____
_____

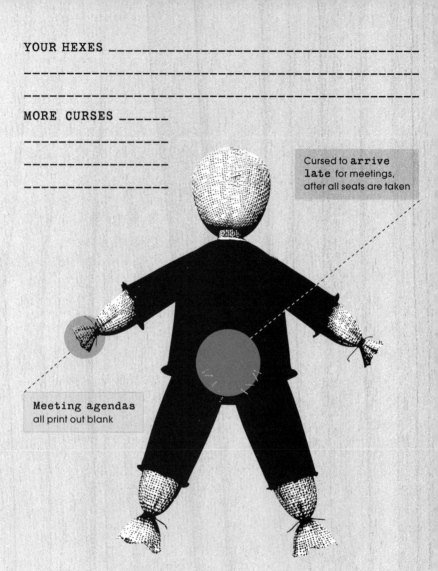

Cursed to **arrive late** for meetings, after all seats are taken

Meeting agendas all print out blank

OFFENDER _____

OFFENSE _____

VOODOO RETRIBUTION _____

_____

_____

_____

_____

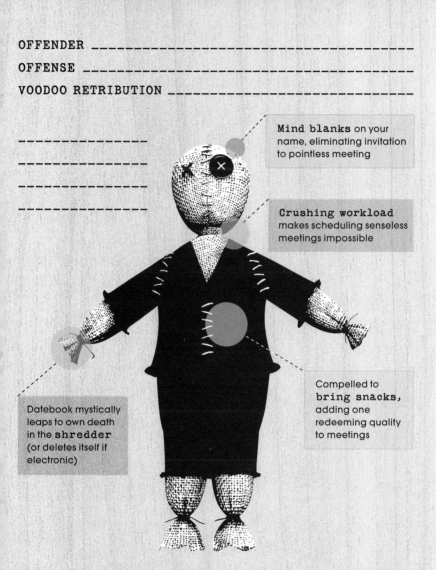

Mind blanks on your name, eliminating invitation to pointless meeting

Crushing workload makes scheduling senseless meetings impossible

Compelled to **bring snacks,** adding one redeeming quality to meetings

Datebook mystically leaps to own death in the **shredder** (or deletes itself if electronic)

*** Check all that apply. Fill in your own spells and incantations. ***

YOUR HEXES _____

_____

_____

MORE CURSES _____

_____

_____

_____

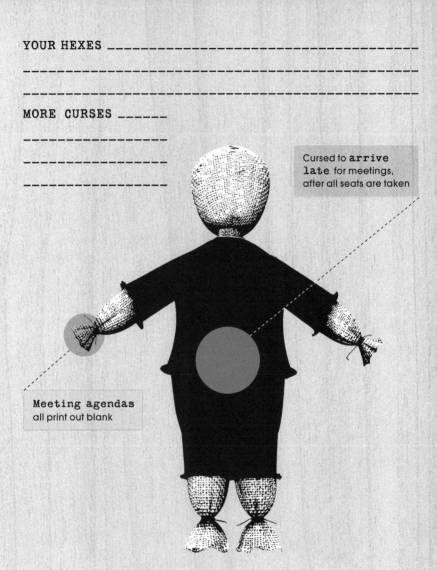

Cursed to **arrive late** for meetings, after all seats are taken

Meeting agendas
all print out blank

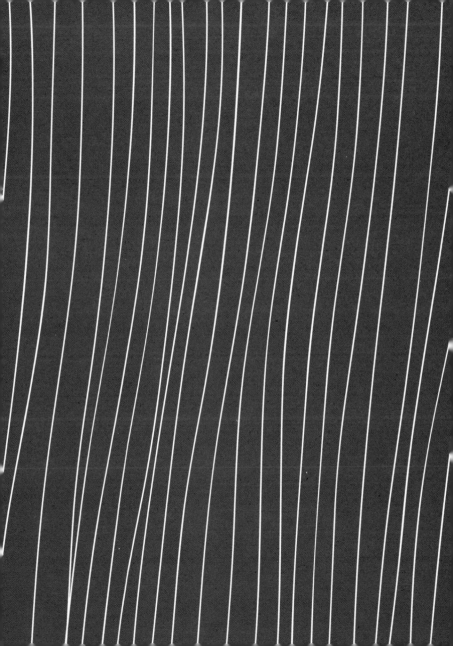

WORK PASSER-ONNER

How is it the Work Passer-Onner is always too busy to do their own work, but they're always the first person out the door?

It's not like you have a mountain of work in your inbox, so why not take on another few projects that will keep you late but won't get you any recognition? Oh wait, your inbox *does* look like Mt. Everest and you *don't* have time to pick up someone else's slack. It's time to put your foot down without having to actually put anything down except some checkmarks on paper. It'll be awfully hard for someone to ask you to do something when they're always swallowing their tongue. And what's this in their inbox? Why it's the exact thing they just passed on, but it's back on them to get their own job done. With everyone else's work out of the way, you'll finally have time to get your own work done and get out of the office at a reasonable hour. The increase in vitamin D from all that sunlight might even cure those rickets that have been plaguing you lately.

OFFENDER _____

OFFENSE _____

VOODOO RETRIBUTION _____

Swallows tongue whenever the words "can you" or "I need you to" begin to form

Amnesia for your desk location and telephone extension

Cyclical enchantment on all work, causing it to **reappear in inbox**

Knee-jerk reaction to pass along mindless work overridden by **Charley horse**

_____

_____

_____

_____

*** Check all that apply. Fill in your own spells and incantations. ***

YOUR HEXES _____

_____

_____

MORE CURSES _____

_____

_____

_____

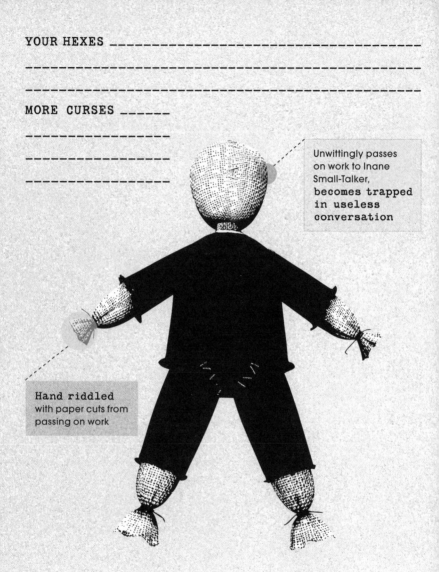

Unwittingly passes on work to Inane Small-Talker, **becomes trapped in useless conversation**

Hand riddled with paper cuts from passing on work

OFFENDER _____

OFFENSE _____

VOODOO RETRIBUTION _____

Swallows tongue
whenever the words
"can you" or "I need you
to" begin to form

Amnesia for your desk location
and telephone extension

Cyclical
enchantment on
all work, causing
it to **reappear
in inbox**

_____

_____

_____

_____

Knee-jerk reaction to
pass along mindless
work overridden by
Charley horse

*** Check all that apply. Fill in your own spells and incantations. ***

YOUR HEXES _____

_____

_____

MORE CURSES _____

_____

_____

_____

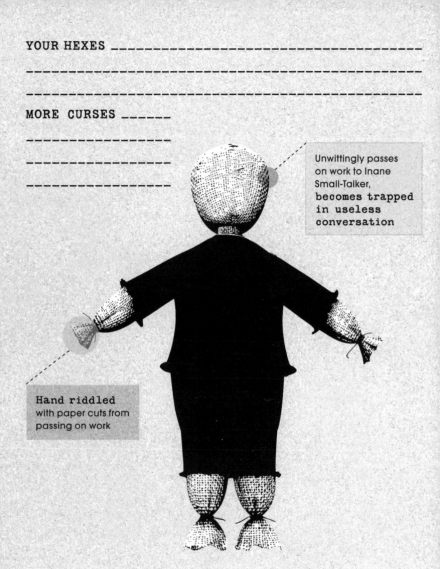

Unwittingly passes on work to Inane Small-Talker, **becomes trapped in useless conversation**

Hand riddled with paper cuts from passing on work

OFFENDER _____

OFFENSE _____

VOODOO RETRIBUTION _____

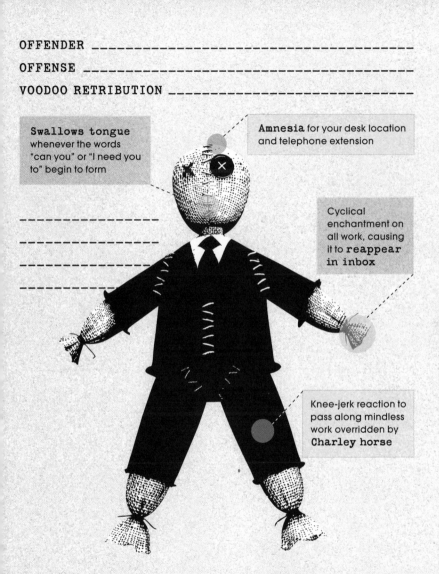

Swallows tongue
whenever the words
"can you" or "I need you
to" begin to form

Amnesia for your desk location
and telephone extension

_____

_____

_____

_____

Cyclical
enchantment on
all work, causing
it to **reappear
in inbox**

Knee-jerk reaction to
pass along mindless
work overridden by
Charley horse

*** Check all that apply. Fill in your own spells and incantations. ***

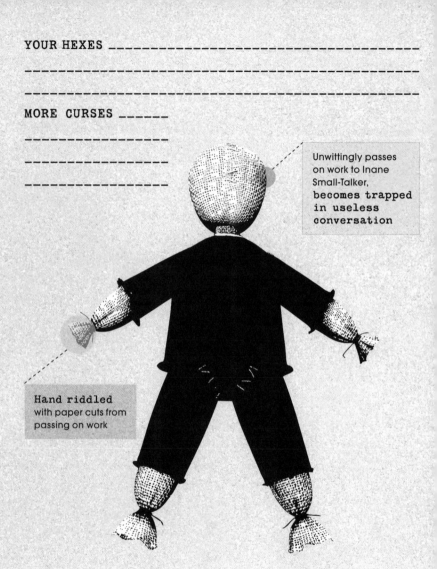

YOUR HEXES _____
_____
_____

MORE CURSES _____
_____
_____
_____

Unwittingly passes on work to Inane Small-Talker, **becomes trapped in useless conversation**

Hand **riddled** with paper cuts from passing on work

OFFENDER _____

OFFENSE _____

VOODOO RETRIBUTION _____

Swallows tongue whenever the words "can you" or "I need you to" begin to form

Amnesia for your desk location and telephone extension

_____

_____

_____

_____

Cyclical enchantment on all work, causing it to **reappear in inbox**

Knee-jerk reaction to pass along mindless work overridden by **Charley horse**

*** Check all that apply. Fill in your own spells and incantations. ***

YOUR HEXES _____

_____

_____

MORE CURSES _____

_____

_____

_____

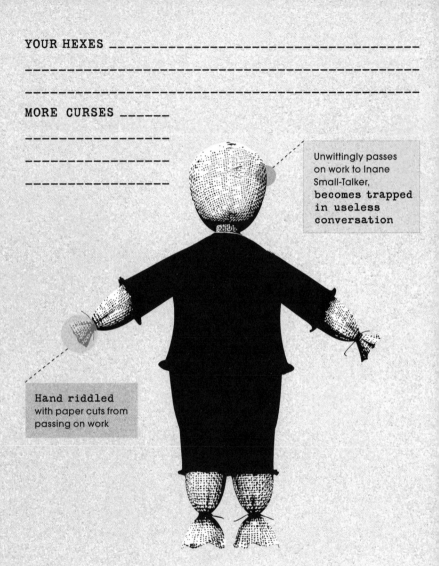

Unwittingly passes on work to Inane Small-Talker, **becomes trapped in useless conversation**

Hand riddled with paper cuts from passing on work

OFFENDER _____

OFFENSE _____

VOODOO RETRIBUTION _____

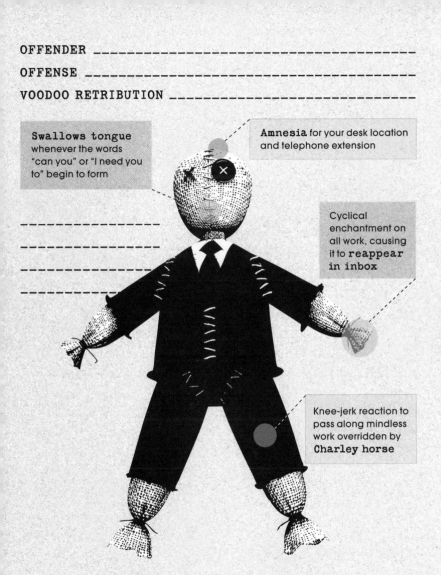

Swallows tongue whenever the words "can you" or "I need you to" begin to form

Amnesia for your desk location and telephone extension

_____

_____

_____

_____

Cyclical enchantment on all work, causing it to **reappear in inbox**

Knee-jerk reaction to pass along mindless work overridden by **Charley horse**

*** Check all that apply. Fill in your own spells and incantations. ***

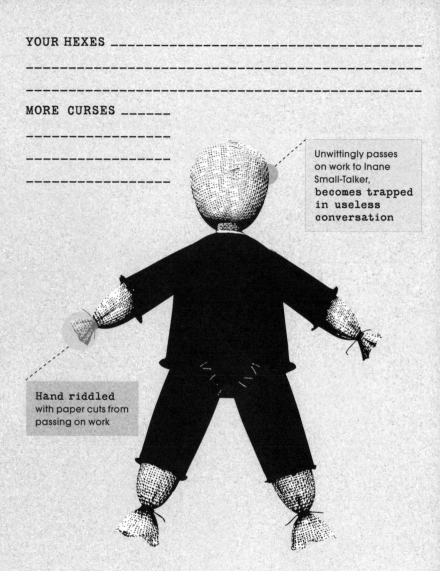

YOUR HEXES _____

_____

_____

MORE CURSES _____

_____

_____

_____

Unwittingly passes on work to Inane Small-Talker, **becomes trapped in useless conversation**

Hand **riddled** with paper cuts from passing on work

OFFENDER _____

OFFENSE _____

VOODOO RETRIBUTION _____

Swallows tongue
whenever the words
"can you" or "I need you
to" begin to form

Amnesia for your desk location
and telephone extension

Cyclical
enchantment on
all work, causing
it to **reappear
in inbox**

_____

_____

_____

_____

Knee-jerk reaction to
pass along mindless
work overridden by
Charley horse

*** Check all that apply. Fill in your own spells and incantations. ***

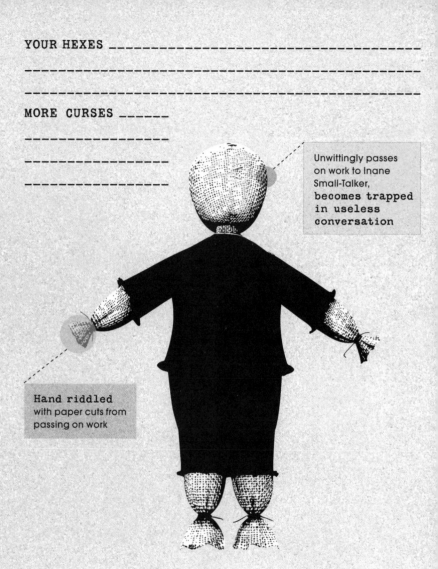

YOUR HEXES _____

_____

_____

MORE CURSES _____

_____

_____

_____

Unwittingly passes on work to Inane Small-Talker, **becomes trapped in useless conversation**

Hand **riddled** with paper cuts from passing on work

OFFENDER _____

OFFENSE _____

VOODOO RETRIBUTION _____

Swallows tongue whenever the words "can you" or "I need you to" begin to form

Amnesia for your desk location and telephone extension

_____

_____

_____

_____

Cyclical enchantment on all work, causing it to **reappear in inbox**

Knee-jerk reaction to pass along mindless work overridden by **Charley horse**

*** Check all that apply. Fill in your own spells and incantations. ***

153

MORE CURSES _____

_____

_____

_____

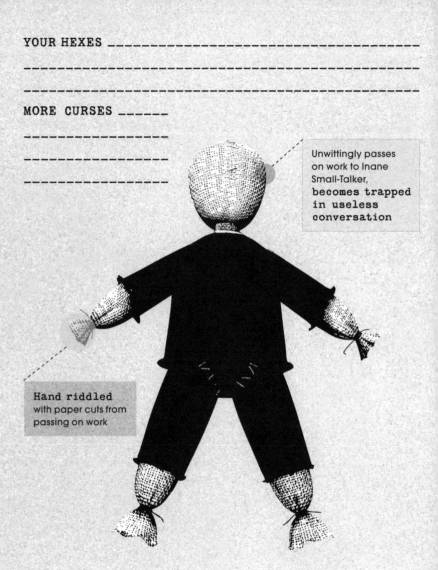

Unwittingly passes on work to Inane Small-Talker, **becomes trapped in useless conversation**

Hand riddled with paper cuts from passing on work

OFFENDER _____

OFFENSE _____

VOODOO RETRIBUTION _____

Swallows tongue
whenever the words
"can you" or "I need you
to" begin to form

Amnesia for your desk location
and telephone extension

Cyclical
enchantment on
all work, causing
it to **reappear
in inbox**

_____

_____

_____

_____

Knee-jerk reaction to
pass along mindless
work overridden by
Charley horse

*** Check all that apply. Fill in your own spells and incantations. ***

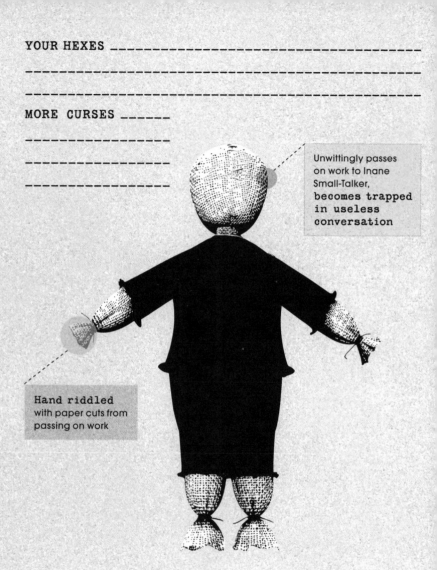

YOUR HEXES _____
_____
_____

MORE CURSES _____
_____
_____
_____

Unwittingly passes on work to Inane Small-Talker, **becomes trapped in useless conversation**

Hand riddled with paper cuts from passing on work

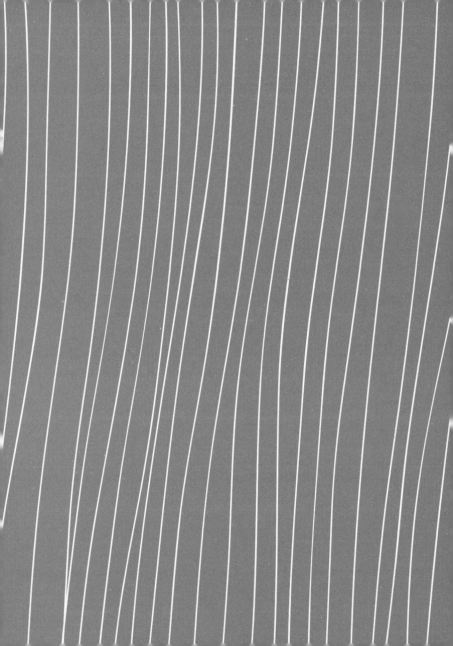

TECH SUPPORT

It's been seven months since you asked tech support to fix your monitor so that everything stops showing up at 25% its normal size, causing your eyesight to deteriorate on the rare days when you're able to see because you don't have a blinding migraine from squinting at your screen.

You've written them emails everyday (or at least you think you have, but you can't be sure since you can't see your dang screen), you've called twice a day leaving messages that range from professional to pleading, and the most you've gotten was an automatic out-of-office reply. It's time to hit IT where it hurts—in their *World of WarCraft* avatars. Next time tech support "misses" your call because they're raiding a dungeon online, ensure that a vat of virtual boiling acid lays their character to rest. If revenge isn't enough, and you want your problem taken care of, a simple check of a circle will compel tech support to answer their phone no matter how much they try to resist it. Even though cc'ing your boss on emails to them may not get results, a little voodoo will get the job done.

Laptop battery **spontaneously combusts**

Compelled to answer phone instead of glancing at caller ID and ignoring it

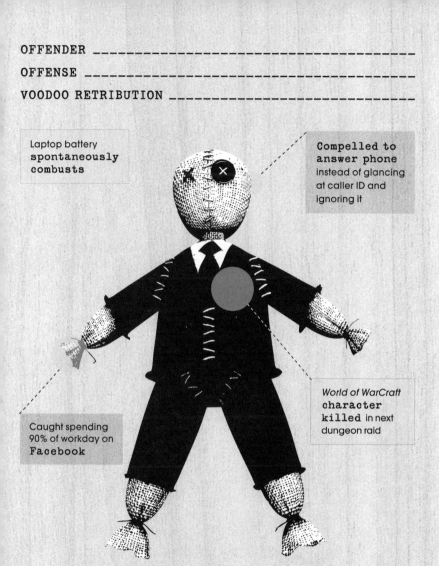

World of WarCraft **character killed** in next dungeon raid

Caught spending 90% of workday on **Facebook**

*** Check all that apply. Fill in your own spells and incantations. ***

YOUR HEXES _____
_____
_____

MORE CURSES _____
_____
_____
_____

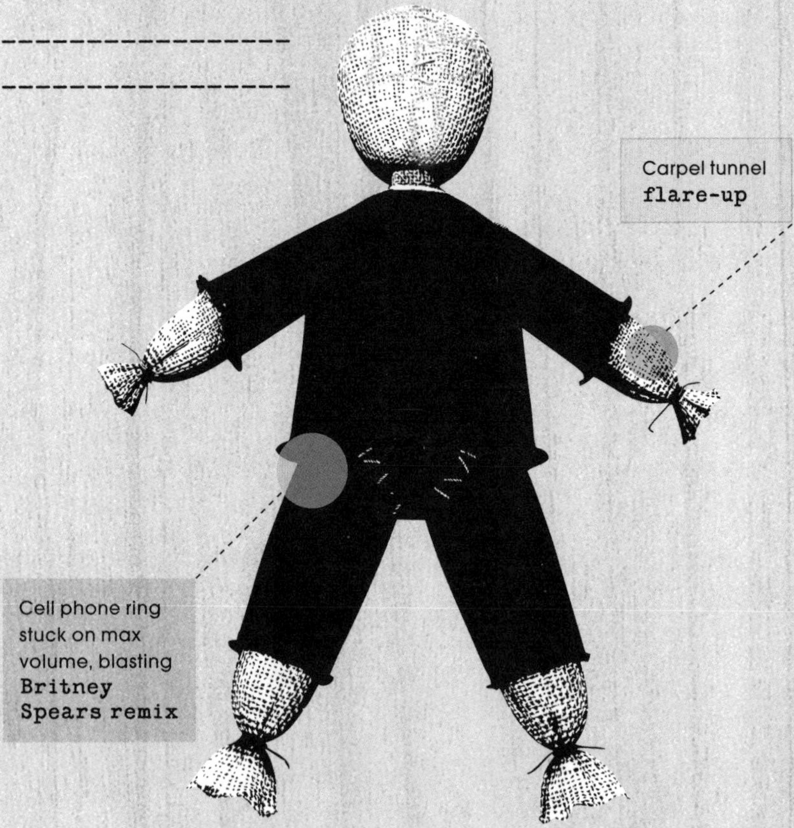

Carpel tunnel **flare-up**

Cell phone ring
stuck on max
volume, blasting
**Britney
Spears remix**

OFFENDER _____

OFFENSE _____

VOODOO RETRIBUTION _____

Laptop battery **spontaneously combusts**

Compelled to answer phone instead of glancing at caller ID and ignoring it

Caught spending 90% of workday on **Facebook**

World of WarCraft **character killed** in next dungeon raid

*** Check all that apply. Fill in your own spells and incantations. ***

YOUR HEXES _____

_____

_____

MORE CURSES _____

_____

_____

_____

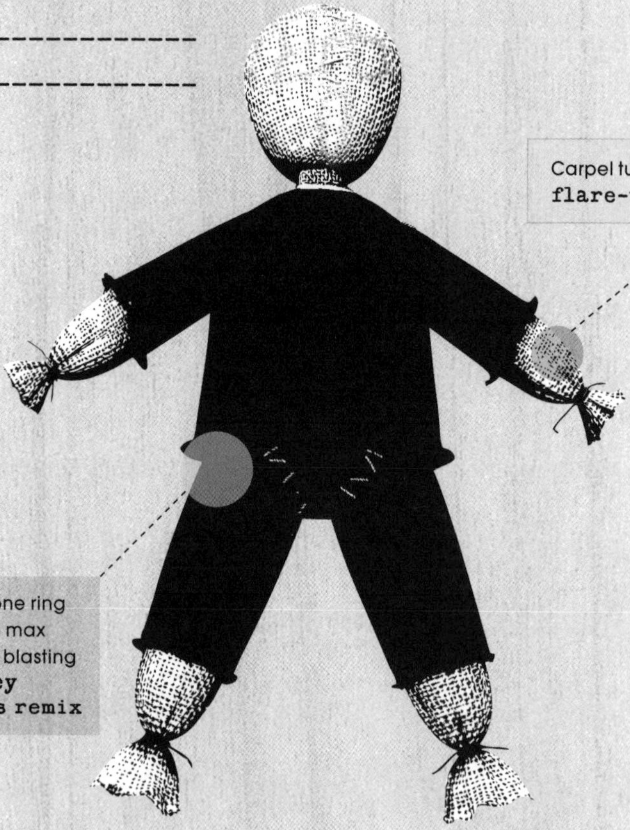

Carpel tunnel
flare-up

Cell phone ring
stuck on max
volume, blasting
**Britney
Spears remix**

OFFENDER _____

OFFENSE _____

VOODOO RETRIBUTION _____

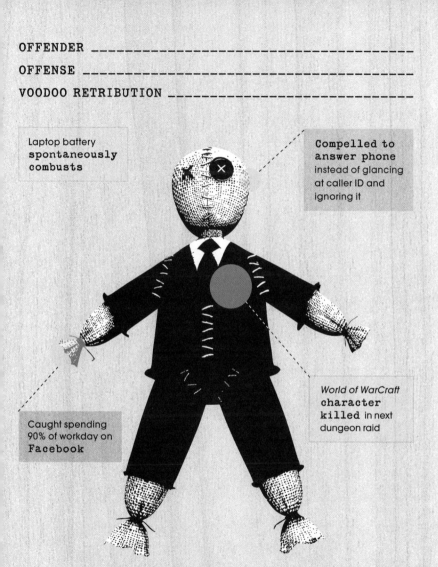

Laptop battery **spontaneously combusts**

Compelled to answer phone instead of glancing at caller ID and ignoring it

World of WarCraft **character killed** in next dungeon raid

Caught spending 90% of workday on **Facebook**

*** Check all that apply. Fill in your own spells and incantations. ***

YOUR HEXES _____
_____
_____

MORE CURSES _____
_____
_____
_____

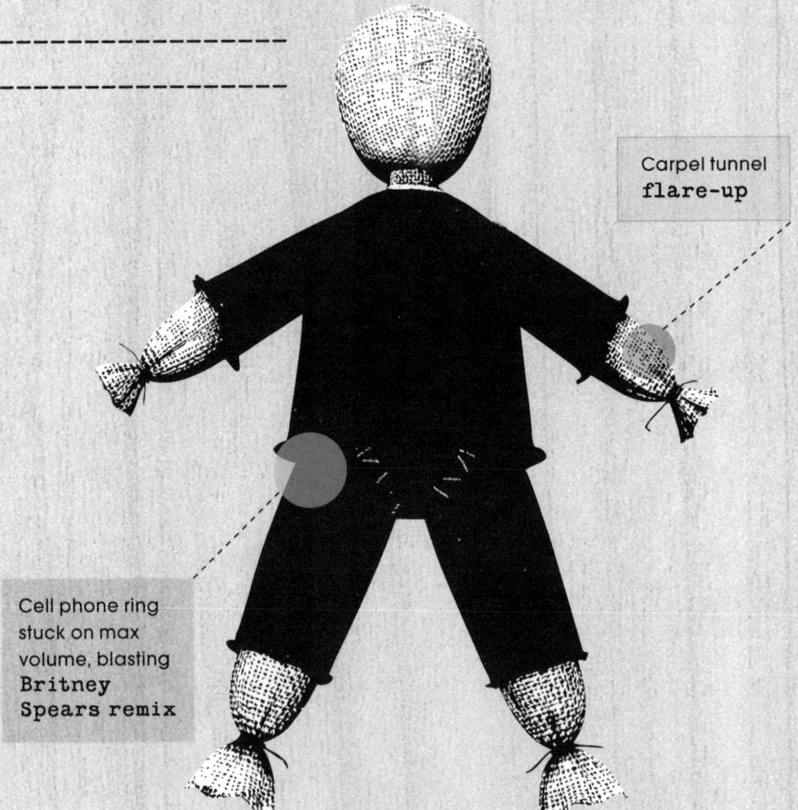

Carpel tunnel **flare-up**

Cell phone ring stuck on max volume, blasting **Britney Spears remix**

164

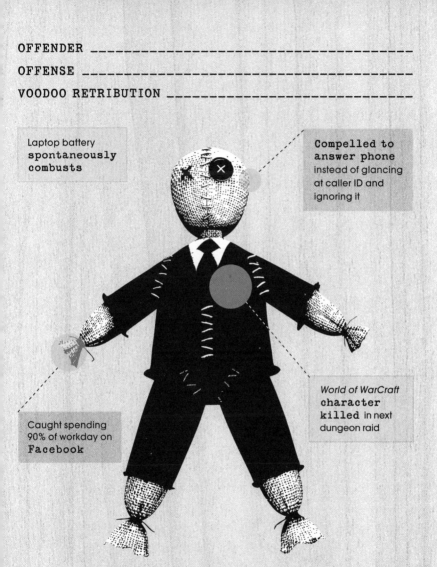

OFFENDER _____

OFFENSE _____

VOODOO RETRIBUTION _____

Laptop battery **spontaneously combusts**

Compelled to answer phone instead of glancing at caller ID and ignoring it

World of WarCraft **character killed** in next dungeon raid

Caught spending 90% of workday on **Facebook**

*** Check all that apply. Fill in your own spells and incantations. ***

165

YOUR HEXES _____
_____
_____

MORE CURSES _____
_____
_____
_____

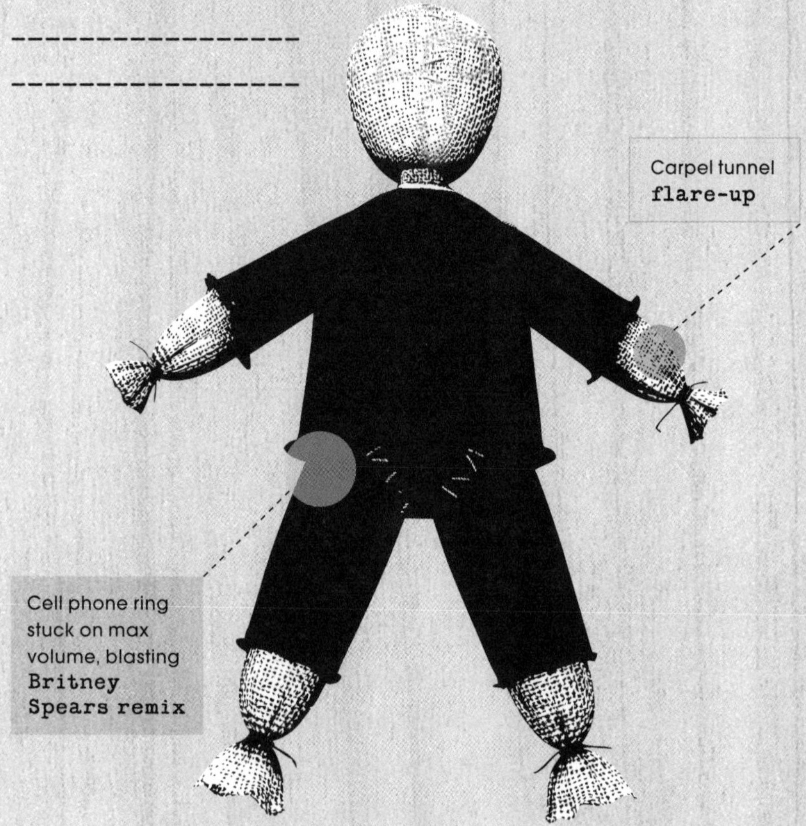

Carpel tunnel **flare-up**

Cell phone ring
stuck on max
volume, blasting
**Britney
Spears remix**

OFFENDER _____

OFFENSE _____

VOODOO RETRIBUTION _____

Laptop battery **spontaneously combusts**

Compelled to answer phone instead of glancing at caller ID and ignoring it

Caught spending 90% of workday on **Facebook**

World of WarCraft **character killed** in next dungeon raid

*** Check all that apply. Fill in your own spells and incantations. ***

YOUR HEXES _____

_____

_____

MORE CURSES _____

_____

_____

_____

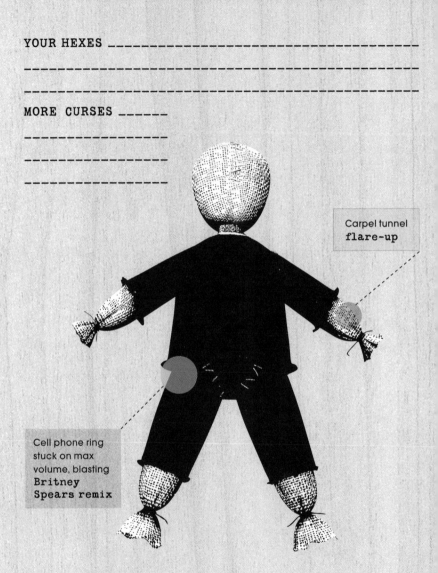

Carpel tunnel
flare-up

Cell phone ring
stuck on max
volume, blasting
**Britney
Spears remix**

OFFENDER _____

OFFENSE _____

VOODOO RETRIBUTION _____

Laptop battery **spontaneously combusts**

Compelled to answer phone instead of glancing at caller ID and ignoring it

World of WarCraft **character killed** in next dungeon raid

Caught spending 90% of workday on **Facebook**

*** Check all that apply. Fill in your own spells and incantations. ***

MORE CURSES _____

_____

_____

_____

Carpel tunnel
flare-up

Cell phone ring
stuck on max
volume, blasting
**Britney
Spears remix**

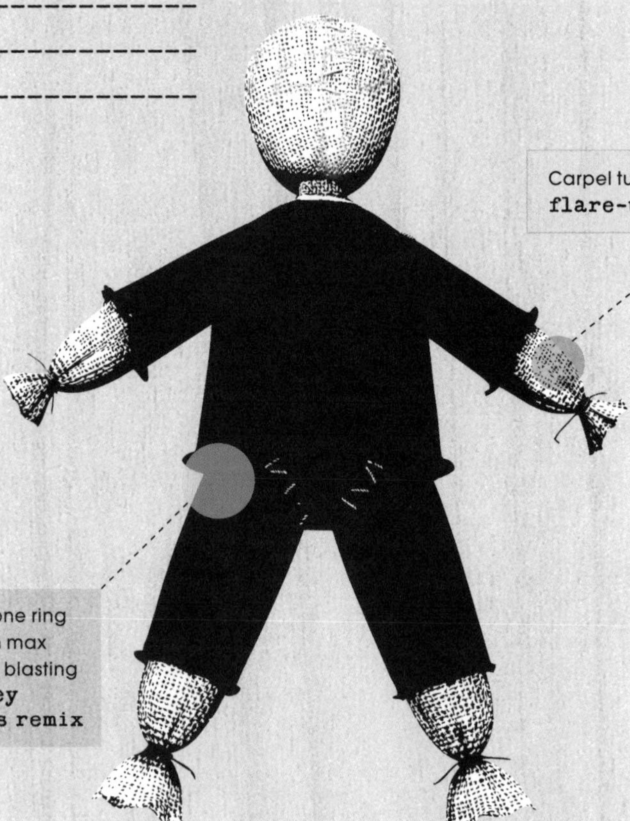

Laptop battery **spontaneously combusts**

Compelled to answer phone instead of glancing at caller ID and ignoring it

Caught spending 90% of workday on **Facebook**

World of WarCraft **character killed** in next dungeon raid

*** Check all that apply. Fill in your own spells and incantations. ***

MORE CURSES _____

_____

_____

_____

Carpel tunnel **flare-up**

Cell phone ring
stuck on max
volume, blasting
**Britney
Spears remix**

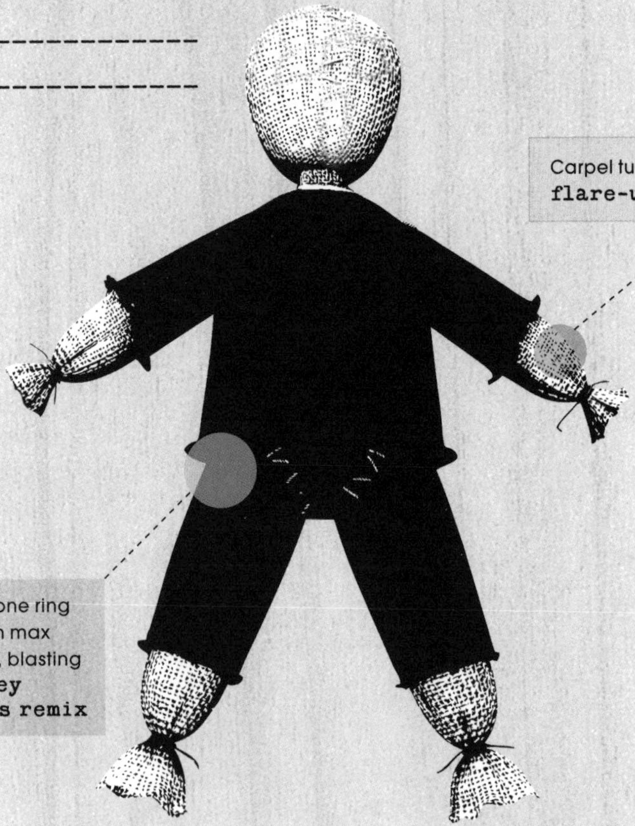

OFFENDER _____

OFFENSE _____

VOODOO RETRIBUTION _____

Laptop battery **spontaneously combusts**

Compelled to answer phone instead of glancing at caller ID and ignoring it

World of WarCraft **character killed** in next dungeon raid

Caught spending 90% of workday on **Facebook**

*** Check all that apply. Fill in your own spells and incantations. ***

YOUR HEXES _____

_____

_____

MORE CURSES _____

_____

_____

_____

Carpel tunnel
flare-up

Cell phone ring
stuck on max
volume, blasting
**Britney
Spears remix**

174

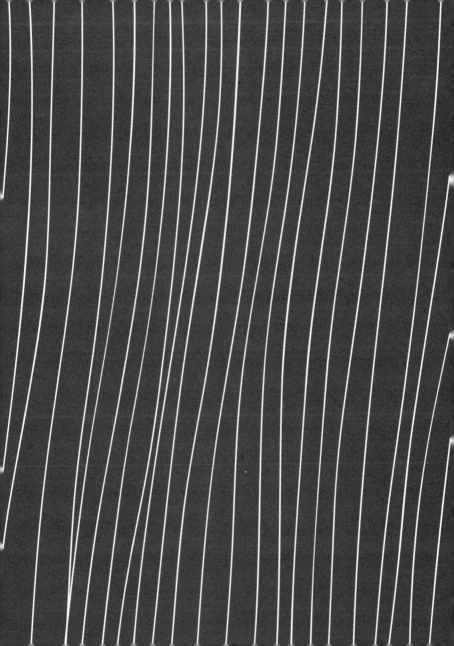

RUMOR-STARTER

OMG! Did you hear that Deborah from accounting was caught making out with Allen from the mailroom in the back elevator?

Did you know that John got sent to HR because he was looking at porn at work? You didn't hear it here, but Mark was totally caught stealing office supplies. Lies! All of them, lies. OK, maybe not the one about John, but the rest are all lies. And even if they aren't, you couldn't care less. Still, everyone is whipped into a fever pitch of whispering and shifty glances when the Rumor-Starter makes their rounds around the office.

Who knows what they're saying about you? Just yesterday I heard that you came in twenty minutes late smelling like cheap vodka. Finally you can do something without lowering yourself to the Rumor-Starter's level. Get even lower than that by voodooing up some tinnitus that rings deafeningly loud in their ears whenever one of their rumors is repeated. Or the next time they want to say something about your boss's trampy wife, make sure they accidentally cc him on it. That'll learn 'em.

OFFENDER _____

OFFENSE _____

VOODOO RETRIBUTION _____

Bewitched tongue sings National Anthem when the words "did you hear" begin to form

Deafening tinnitus whenever a rumor is repeated

Accidentally cc's target of next rumor

Compelled to perform **chicken dance** whenever a rumor is started

_____

_____

_____

_____

*** Check all that apply. Fill in your own spells and incantations. ***

YOUR HEXES _____

_____

_____

MORE CURSES _____

_____

_____

_____

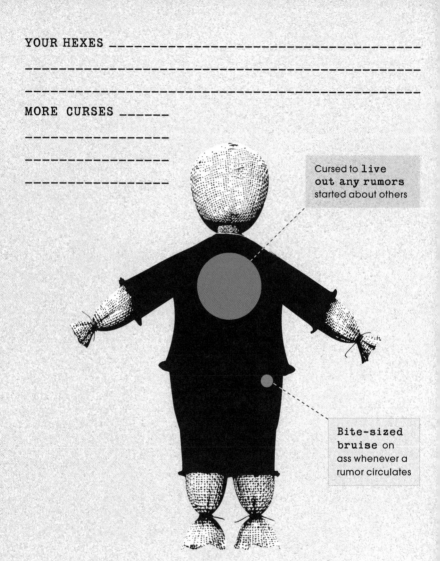

Cursed to **live out any rumors** started about others

Bite-sized bruise on ass whenever a rumor circulates

OFFENDER _____

OFFENSE _____

VOODOO RETRIBUTION _____

Bewitched tongue sings National Anthem when the words "did you hear" begin to form

Deafening tinnitus whenever a rumor is repeated

Accidentally cc's target of next rumor

Compelled to perform **chicken dance** whenever a rumor is started

_____

_____

_____

_____

*** Check all that apply. Fill in your own spells and incantations. ***

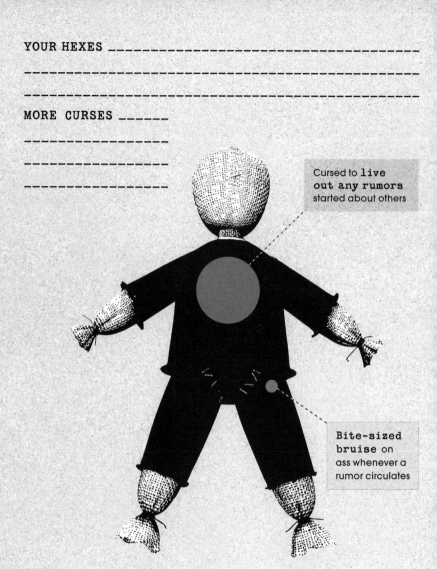

YOUR HEXES _____

_____

_____

MORE CURSES _____

_____

_____

_____

Cursed to **live out any rumors** started about others

Bite-sized bruise on ass whenever a rumor circulates

OFFENDER _____

OFFENSE _____

VOODOO RETRIBUTION _____

Deafening tinnitus whenever a rumor is repeated

Bewitched tongue sings National Anthem when the words "did you hear" begin to form

Accidentally cc's target of next rumor

_____
_____
_____
_____

Compelled to perform **chicken dance** whenever a rumor is started

*** Check all that apply. Fill in your own spells and incantations. ***

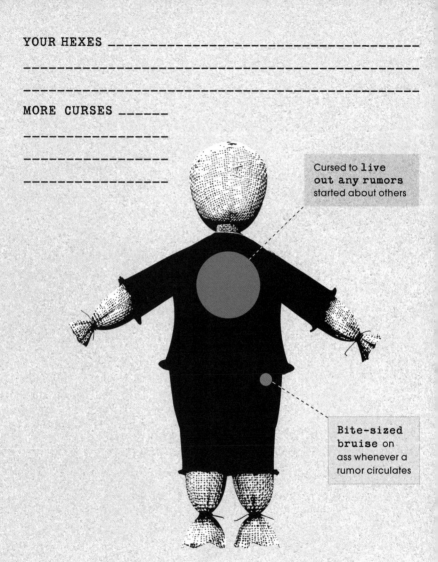

YOUR HEXES _____

_____

_____

MORE CURSES _____

_____

_____

_____

Cursed to **live out any rumors** started about others

Bite-sized bruise on ass whenever a rumor circulates

OFFENDER _____

OFFENSE _____

VOODOO RETRIBUTION _____

Deafening tinnitus whenever a rumor is repeated

Bewitched tongue sings National Anthem when the words "did you hear" begin to form

Accidentally cc's target of next rumor

Compelled to perform **chicken dance** whenever a rumor is started

_____

_____

_____

_____

*** Check all that apply. Fill in your own spells and incantations. ***

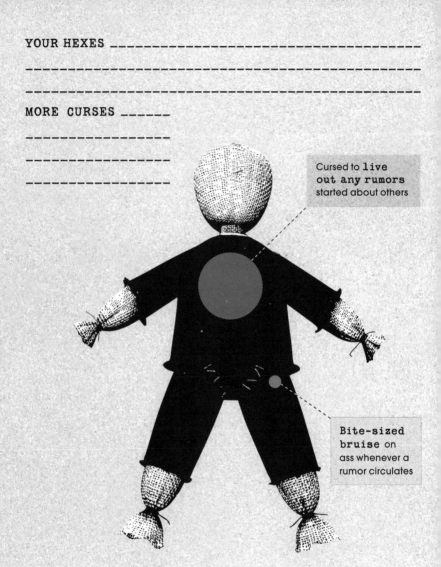

YOUR HEXES _____
_____
_____

MORE CURSES _____
_____
_____
_____

Cursed to **live out any rumors** started about others

Bite-sized bruise on ass whenever a rumor circulates

OFFENDER _____

OFFENSE _____

VOODOO RETRIBUTION _____

Bewitched tongue sings National Anthem when the words "did you hear" begin to form

Deafening tinnitus whenever a rumor is repeated

Accidentally cc's target of next rumor

_____

_____

_____

_____

Compelled to perform **chicken dance** whenever a rumor is started

*** Check all that apply. Fill in your own spells and incantations. ***

YOUR HEXES _____
_____
_____

MORE CURSES _____
_____
_____
_____

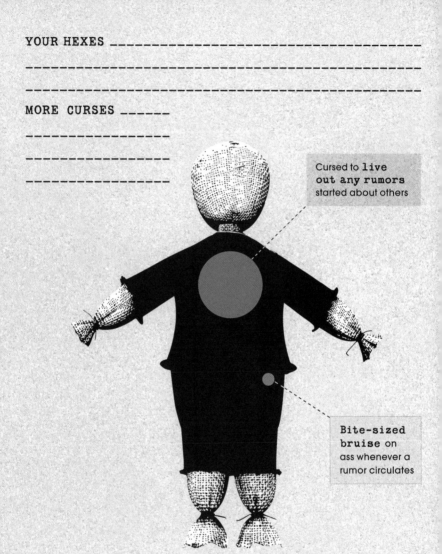

Cursed to **live out any rumors** started about others

Bite-sized bruise on ass whenever a rumor circulates

OFFENDER _____

OFFENSE _____

VOODOO RETRIBUTION _____

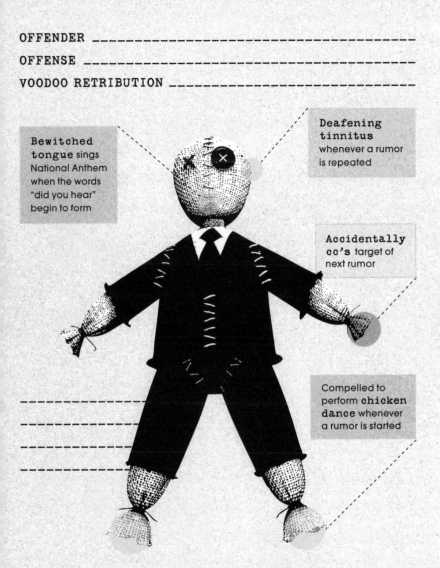

Bewitched tongue sings National Anthem when the words "did you hear" begin to form

Deafening tinnitus whenever a rumor is repeated

Accidentally cc's target of next rumor

Compelled to perform **chicken dance** whenever a rumor is started

_____

_____

_____

_____

*** Check all that apply. Fill in your own spells and incantations. ***

YOUR HEXES _____

_____

_____

MORE CURSES _____

_____

_____

_____

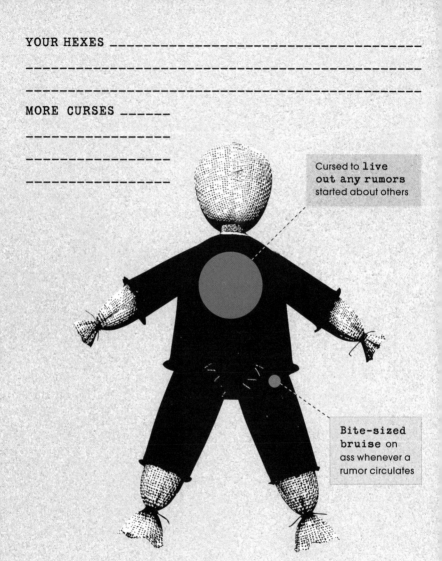

Cursed to **live out any rumors** started about others

Bite-sized bruise on ass whenever a rumor circulates

OFFENDER _____

OFFENSE _____

VOODOO RETRIBUTION _____

Bewitched tongue sings National Anthem when the words "did you hear" begin to form

Deafening tinnitus whenever a rumor is repeated

Accidentally cc's target of next rumor

Compelled to perform **chicken dance** whenever a rumor is started

_____

_____

_____

_____

*** Check all that apply. Fill in your own spells and incantations. ***

YOUR HEXES _____

_____

_____

MORE CURSES _____

_____

_____

_____

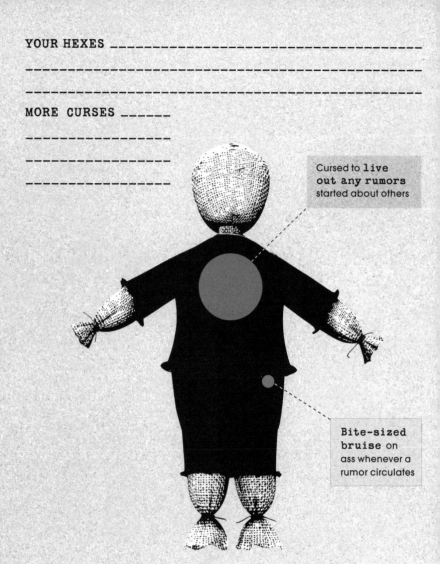

Cursed to **live out any rumors** started about others

Bite-sized bruise on ass whenever a rumor circulates

OFFENDER _____

OFFENSE _____

VOODOO RETRIBUTION _____

Bewitched tongue sings National Anthem when the words "did you hear" begin to form

Deafening tinnitus whenever a rumor is repeated

Accidentally cc's target of next rumor

Compelled to perform **chicken dance** whenever a rumor is started

_____

_____

_____

_____

*** Check all that apply. Fill in your own spells and incantations. ***

YOUR HEXES _____
_____
_____
MORE CURSES _____
_____
_____
_____

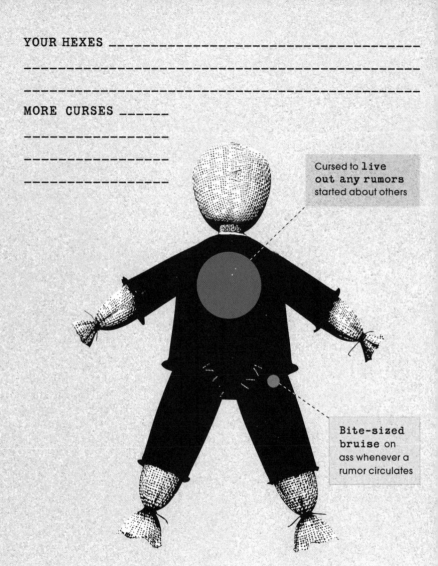

Cursed to **live out any rumors** started about others

Bite-sized bruise on ass whenever a rumor circulates

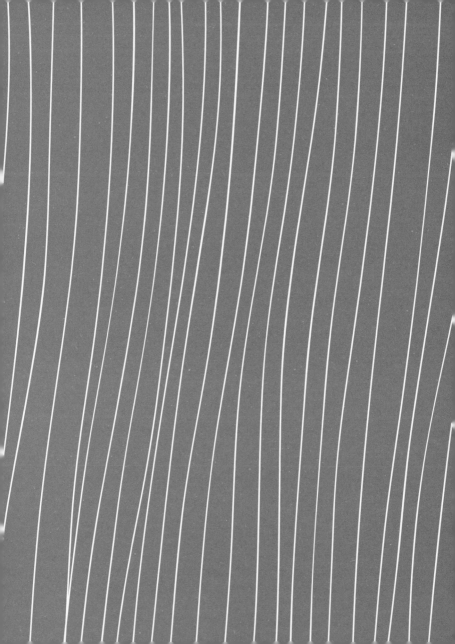

"I'LL GET BACK TO YOU" LIAR

This deceitful, lying liar has made you late on countless projects, all because you needed just one tiny snippet of information from them, and they never got back to you.

Anything you ask them for, they always tell you, "I'll get back to you on that." And they don't. Even if it's the simplest little thing, like "When's your birthday?" or "Can I borrow a pen?" the answer is always the same: "I'll get back to you."

If you really, truly, and desperately need something, you have to hunt them down—resisting the urge to cross your arms and tap your foot once you find them—and refuse to budge until they hand it over. Even though seeing them sweat in this situation is sort of pleasant, you don't have time to chase them all over the office. Save yourself some aggravation and energy by jinxing their hand to immediately hit "Reply" whenever they read an email. Next time they walk past and you ask a question, confound their feet so they're pinned to the floor next to your desk. After you do, you won't know how you ever survived without black magic.

OFFENDER _____

OFFENSE _____

VOODOO RETRIBUTION _____

Compelled to **share all the information** as soon as it is asked for

Doomed to forget family member's faces whenever info is withheld

_____
_____
_____

Chest tightens when more than one hour passes without returning phone calls

Immediately **hits "Reply"** when any email is read

Feet pinned to the floor when walking past someone with a question

*** Check all that apply. Fill in your own spells and incantations. ***

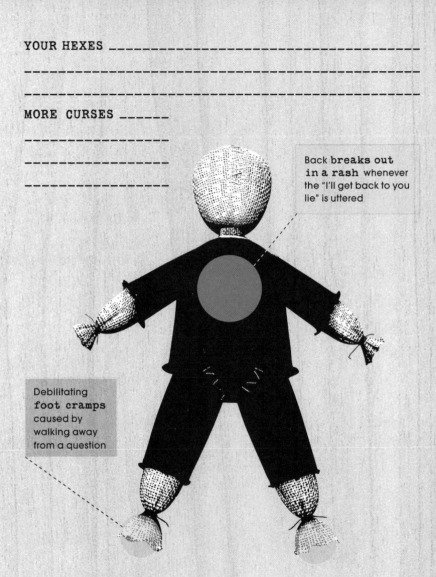

YOUR HEXES _____
_____
_____

MORE CURSES _____
_____
_____
_____

Back **breaks out in a rash** whenever the "I'll get back to you lie" is uttered

Debilitating **foot cramps** caused by walking away from a question

OFFENDER _____

OFFENSE _____

VOODOO RETRIBUTION _____

Compelled to **share all the information** as soon as it is asked for

Doomed to forget family member's faces whenever info is withheld

_____

_____

_____

Chest tightens when more than one hour passes without returning phone calls

Immediately **hits "Reply"** when any email is read

Feet pinned to the floor when walking past someone with a question

*** Check all that apply. Fill in your own spells and incantations. ***

YOUR HEXES _____

_____

_____

MORE CURSES _____

_____

_____

_____

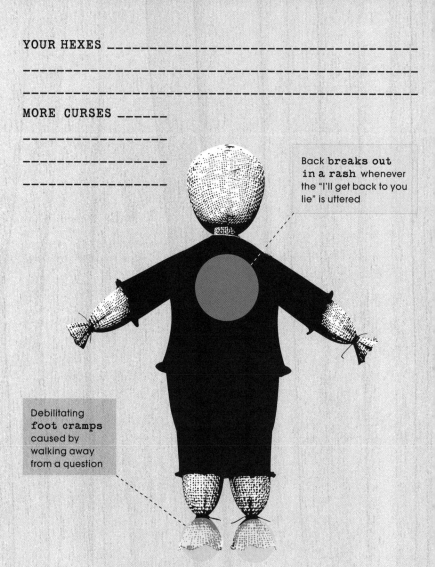

Back **breaks out in a rash** whenever the "I'll get back to you lie" is uttered

Debilitating **foot cramps** caused by walking away from a question

OFFENDER _____

OFFENSE _____

VOODOO RETRIBUTION _____

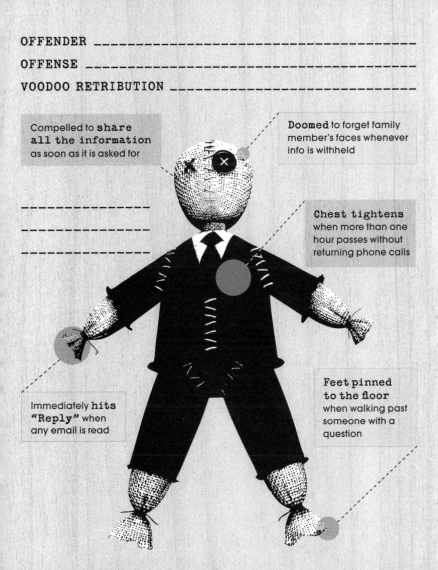

Compelled to **share all the information** as soon as it is asked for

Doomed to forget family member's faces whenever info is withheld

_____
_____
_____

Chest tightens when more than one hour passes without returning phone calls

Immediately **hits "Reply"** when any email is read

Feet pinned to the floor when walking past someone with a question

*** Check all that apply. Fill in your own spells and incantations. ***

YOUR HEXES _____
_____
_____

MORE CURSES _____
_____
_____
_____

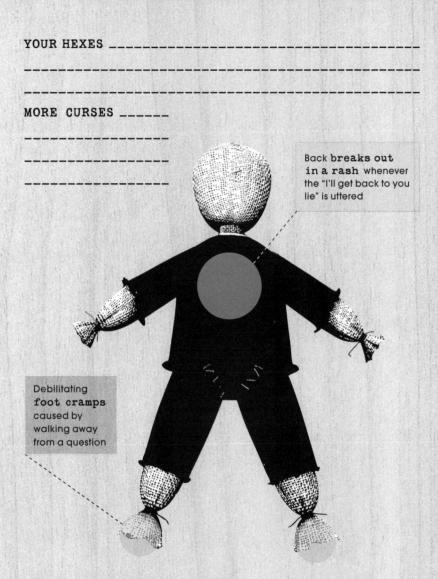

Back **breaks out in a rash** whenever the "I'll get back to you lie" is uttered

Debilitating **foot cramps** caused by walking away from a question

OFFENDER _____

OFFENSE _____

VOODOO RETRIBUTION _____

Compelled to **share all the information** as soon as it is asked for

Doomed to forget family member's faces whenever info is withheld

_____
_____
_____

Chest tightens when more than one hour passes without returning phone calls

Immediately **hits "Reply"** when any email is read

Feet pinned to the floor when walking past someone with a question

*** Check all that apply. Fill in your own spells and incantations. ***

201

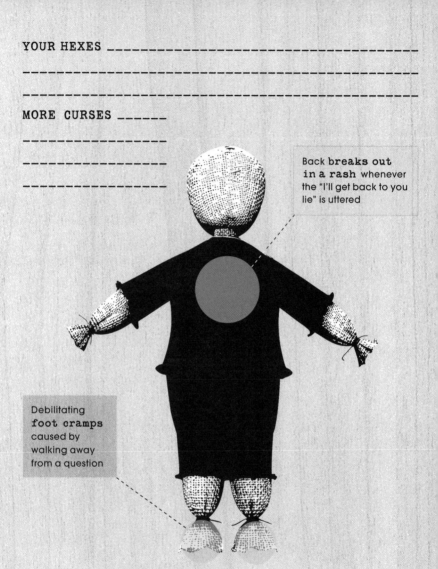

YOUR HEXES _____

_____

_____

MORE CURSES _____

_____

_____

_____

Back **breaks out in a rash** whenever the "I'll get back to you lie" is uttered

Debilitating **foot cramps** caused by walking away from a question

OFFENDER _____

OFFENSE _____

VOODOO RETRIBUTION _____

Compelled to **share all the information** as soon as it is asked for

Doomed to forget family member's faces whenever info is withheld

_____
_____
_____

Chest tightens when more than one hour passes without returning phone calls

Immediately **hits "Reply"** when any email is read

Feet pinned to the floor when walking past someone with a question

*** Check all that apply. Fill in your own spells and incantations. ***

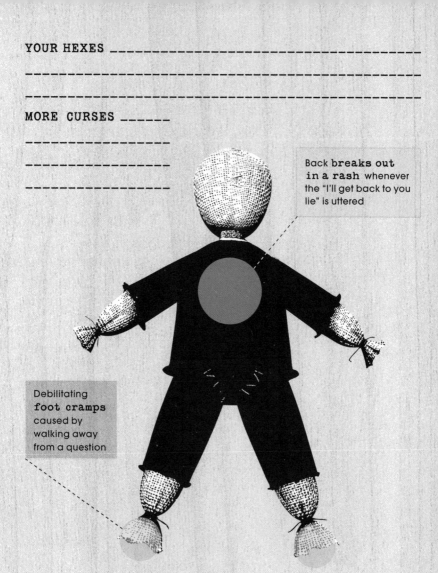

YOUR HEXES _____
_____
_____

MORE CURSES _____
_____
_____
_____

Back **breaks out in a rash** whenever the "I'll get back to you lie" is uttered

Debilitating **foot cramps** caused by walking away from a question

OFFENDER _____

OFFENSE _____

VOODOO RETRIBUTION _____

Compelled to **share
all the information**
as soon as it is asked for

Doomed to forget family
member's faces whenever
info is withheld

_____
_____
_____

Chest tightens
when more than one
hour passes without
returning phone calls

Immediately **hits
"Reply"** when
any email is read

**Feet pinned
to the floor**
when walking past
someone with a
question

*** Check all that apply. Fill in your own spells and incantations. ***

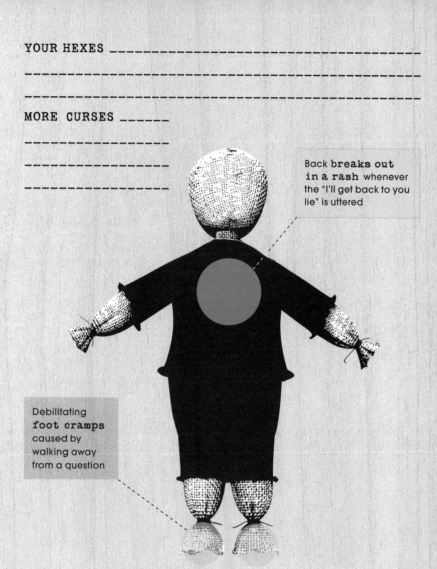

YOUR HEXES _____
_____
_____

MORE CURSES _____
_____
_____
_____

Back **breaks out in a rash** whenever the "I'll get back to you lie" is uttered

Debilitating **foot cramps** caused by walking away from a question

OFFENDER _____

OFFENSE _____

VOODOO RETRIBUTION _____

Compelled to **share all the information** as soon as it is asked for

Doomed to forget family member's faces whenever info is withheld

_____

_____

_____

Chest tightens when more than one hour passes without returning phone calls

Immediately **hits "Reply"** when any email is read

Feet pinned to the floor when walking past someone with a question

*** Check all that apply. Fill in your own spells and incantations. ***

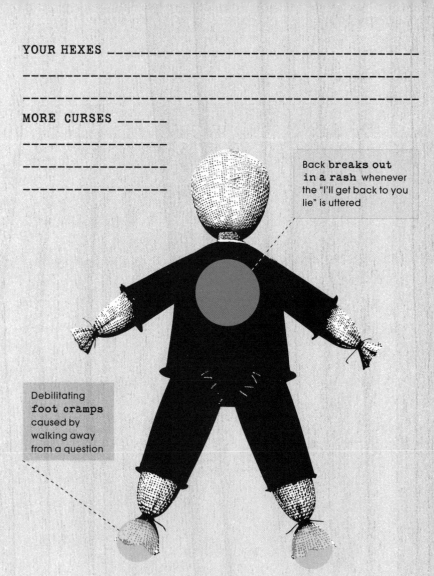

YOUR HEXES _
_ _
_ _

MORE CURSES _ _ _ _ _ _
_ _ _ _ _ _ _ _ _ _ _ _ _ _ _ _
_ _ _ _ _ _ _ _ _ _ _ _ _ _ _ _
_ _ _ _ _ _ _ _ _ _ _ _ _ _ _ _

Back **breaks out in a rash** whenever the "I'll get back to you lie" is uttered

Debilitating **foot cramps** caused by walking away from a question

OFFENDER _____

OFFENSE _____

VOODOO RETRIBUTION _____

Compelled to **share all the information** as soon as it is asked for

Doomed to forget family member's faces whenever info is withheld

_____
_____
_____

Chest tightens when more than one hour passes without returning phone calls

Immediately **hits "Reply"** when any email is read

Feet pinned to the floor when walking past someone with a question

*** Check all that apply. Fill in your own spells and incantations. ***

209

YOUR HEXES _____

_____

_____

MORE CURSES _____

_____

_____

_____

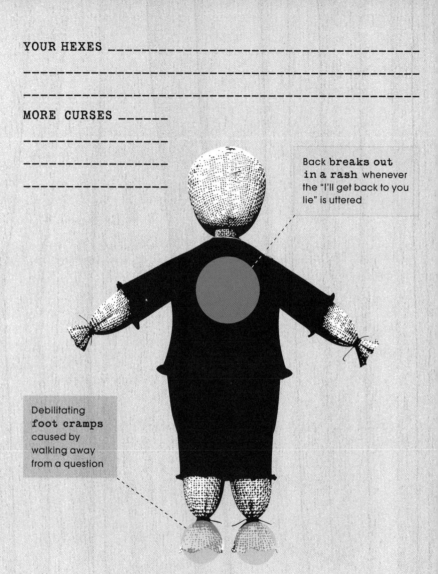

Back **breaks out in a rash** whenever the "I'll get back to you lie" is uttered

Debilitating **foot cramps** caused by walking away from a question

CO-WORKER

This blank doll is for everyone in your office that hasn't been covered in this book.

There are so many agitators, slackers, nuisances, and cretins that you have to deal with, that they couldn't all possibly be named in one book. So this is your chance to fill in the blanks. Pick the person you detest the most, and tailor your own voodoo that's perfectly suited to them. Maybe it's some creep in HR that is hung up on forcing everyone to do an on-site jazzercise class, or a cafeteria worker that you're absolutely positive lacks the hygiene necessary to handle food. Anyone at all can fall under your spells, and once they do, you'll finally have a pleasant and conducive work environment—or at least one that doesn't induce binge drinking.

OFFENDER _____

OFFENSE _____

VOODOO RETRIBUTION _____

_____
_____
_____
_____
_____

*** Check all that apply. Fill in your own spells and incantations. ***

YOUR HEXES _____
_____
_____

MORE CURSES _____
_____
_____
_____

OFFENDER _____

OFFENSE _____

VOODOO RETRIBUTION _____

_____

_____

_____

_____

_____

*** Check all that apply. Fill in your own spells and incantations. ***

YOUR HEXES _____
_____
_____

MORE CURSES _____
_____
_____
_____

OFFENDER _____

OFFENSE _____

VOODOO RETRIBUTION _____

_____
_____
_____
_____
_____

*** Check all that apply. Fill in your own spells and incantations. ***

YOUR HEXES _____

_____

_____

MORE CURSES _____

_____

_____

_____

OFFENDER _____

OFFENSE _____

VOODOO RETRIBUTION _____

_____

_____

_____

_____

_____

*** Check all that apply. Fill in your own spells and incantations. ***

YOUR HEXES _____
_____
_____

MORE CURSES _____
_____
_____
_____

OFFENDER _____

OFFENSE _____

VOODOO RETRIBUTION _____

_____

_____

_____

_____

_____

*** Check all that apply. Fill in your own spells and incantations. ***

YOUR HEXES _____
_____
_____

MORE CURSES _____
_____
_____
_____

OFFENDER _____

OFFENSE _____

VOODOO RETRIBUTION _____

_____
_____
_____
_____
_____

*** Check all that apply. Fill in your own spells and incantations. ***

YOUR HEXES _____
_____
_____
MORE CURSES _____
_____
_____
_____

OFFENDER _____

OFFENSE _____

VOODOO RETRIBUTION _____

_____
_____
_____
_____
_____

*** Check all that apply. Fill in your own spells and incantations. ***

YOUR HEXES _____
_____
_____

MORE CURSES _____
_____
_____
_____

OFFENDER _____

OFFENSE _____

VOODOO RETRIBUTION _____

_____

_____

_____

_____

_____

*** Check all that apply. Fill in your own spells and incantations. ***

YOUR HEXES _____
_____
_____

MORE CURSES _____
_____
_____
_____

228

OFFENDER _____

OFFENSE _____

VOODOO RETRIBUTION _____

_____

_____

_____

_____

_____

*** Check all that apply. Fill in your own spells and incantations. ***

YOUR HEXES _____

_____

_____

MORE CURSES _____

_____

_____

_____

OFFENDER _____

OFFENSE _____

VOODOO RETRIBUTION _____

_____

_____

_____

_____

_____

*** Check all that apply. Fill in your own spells and incantations. ***

YOUR HEXES ______________________________________

____

____

MORE CURSES ______

____

____

____

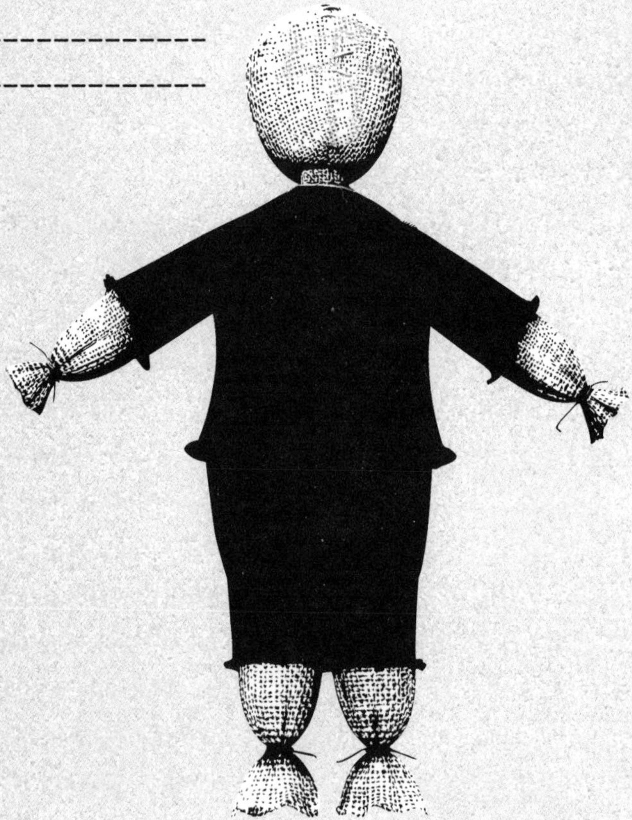

OFFENDER _____

OFFENSE _____

VOODOO RETRIBUTION _____

_____

_____

_____

_____

_____

*** Check all that apply. Fill in your own spells and incantations. ***

YOUR HEXES _____
_____
_____

MORE CURSES _____
_____
_____
_____

OFFENDER _____

OFFENSE _____

VOODOO RETRIBUTION _____

_____

_____

_____

_____

_____

*** Check all that apply. Fill in your own spells and incantations. ***

235

YOUR HEXES _____

_____

_____

MORE CURSES _____

_____

_____

_____

OFFENDER _____

OFFENSE _____

VOODOO RETRIBUTION _____

_____
_____
_____
_____
_____

*** Check all that apply. Fill in your own spells and incantations. ***

YOUR HEXES _____
_____
_____

MORE CURSES _____
_____
_____
_____

OFFENDER _____

OFFENSE _____

VOODOO RETRIBUTION _____

_____

_____

_____

_____

_____

*** Check all that apply. Fill in your own spells and incantations. ***

YOUR HEXES _____
_____
_____

MORE CURSES _____
_____
_____
_____

OFFENDER _____

OFFENSE _____

VOODOO RETRIBUTION _____

_____
_____
_____
_____
_____

*** Check all that apply. Fill in your own spells and incantations. ***

YOUR HEXES _____
_____
_____

MORE CURSES _____
_____
_____
_____

OFFENDER _____

OFFENSE _____

VOODOO RETRIBUTION _____

_____

_____

_____

_____

_____

*** Check all that apply. Fill in your own spells and incantations. ***

YOUR HEXES _____

_____

_____

MORE CURSES _____

_____

_____

_____

244

OFFENDER _____

OFFENSE _____

VOODOO RETRIBUTION _____

*** Check all that apply. Fill in your own spells and incantations. ***

YOUR HEXES _____
_____
_____

MORE CURSES _____
_____
_____
_____

OFFENDER _____

OFFENSE _____

VOODOO RETRIBUTION _____

_____

_____

_____

_____

_____

*** Check all that apply. Fill in your own spells and incantations. ***

YOUR HEXES _____

_____

_____

MORE CURSES _____

_____

_____

_____

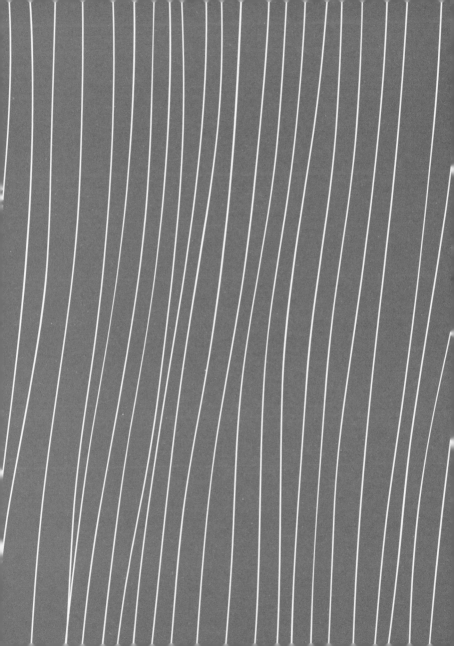

YOU ON A BIG DAY

This is it. Your big day.
Your chance out of your current
hellhole and into a whole new hellhole that might be in a higher
and less painful circle of hell.

You've printed out your résumé on ivory résumé paper, you've
practiced answering the top ten interview questions from
Monster.com, and you've spent a week's salary on an impressive
new suit. All you need, besides your incredible intelligence and
charm, is a little help from the office gods. Oh, almighty and
powerful deities, we beseech you to shine your glory down upon
this humble and impressively qualified applicant! Ensure they're
mind is clear and as sharp as the creases in their immaculately
pressed suit. Cast naught but brilliant words into their mouth, and in
your divine strength give them the posture of a statue, which they
will surely erect in your honor once their new job is secured!

There, that should do it. Now go get 'em, killer!

YOUR NAME _____

ADVANCEMENT DESIRED _____

VOODOO ASSISTANCE _____

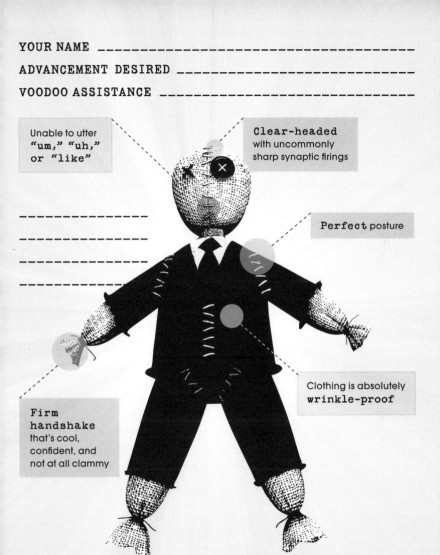

Unable to utter
"um," "uh,"
or "like"

Clear-headed
with uncommonly
sharp synaptic firings

_____
_____
_____
_____

Perfect posture

**Firm
handshake**
that's cool,
confident, and
not at all clammy

Clothing is absolutely
wrinkle-proof

*** Check all that apply. Fill in your own spells and incantations. ***

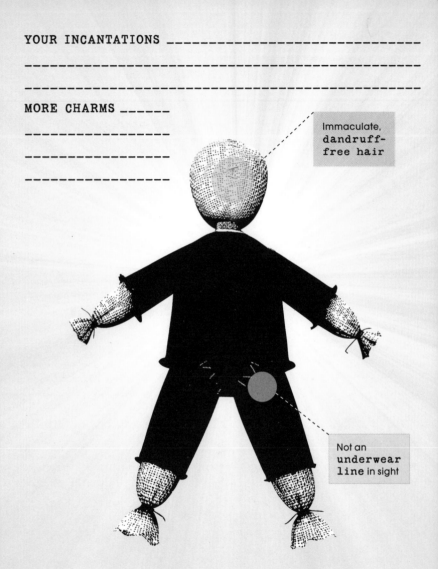

YOUR INCANTATIONS _____
_____
_____

MORE CHARMS _____
_____
_____
_____

Immaculate, **dandruff-free hair**

Not an **underwear line** in sight

YOUR NAME _____

ADVANCEMENT DESIRED _____

VOODOO ASSISTANCE _____

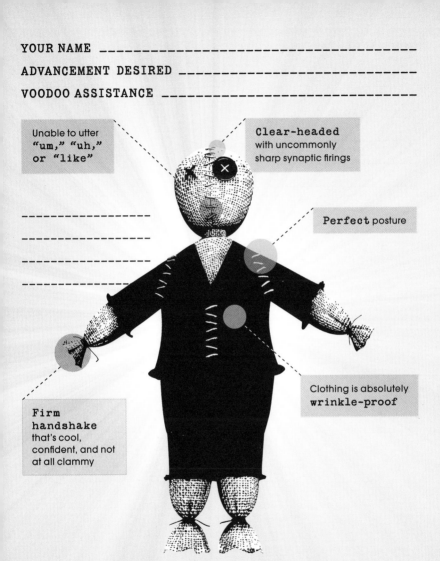

Unable to utter
"um," "uh," or **"like"**

Clear-headed
with uncommonly
sharp synaptic firings

_____
_____
_____
_____

Perfect posture

Clothing is absolutely
wrinkle-proof

Firm handshake
that's cool,
confident, and not
at all clammy

*** Check all that apply. Fill in your own spells and incantations. ***

YOUR INCANTATIONS _____
_____
_____

MORE CHARMS _____
_____
_____
_____

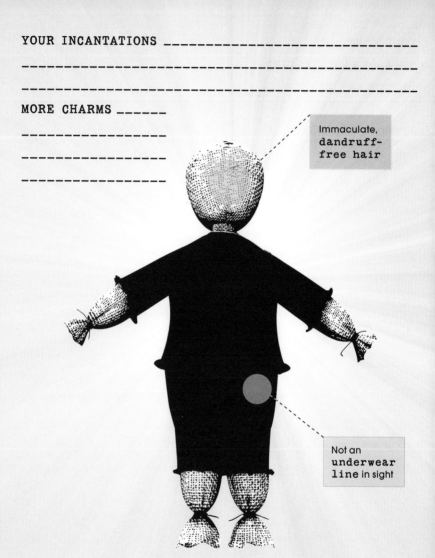

Immaculate, **dandruff-free hair**

Not an **underwear line** in sight

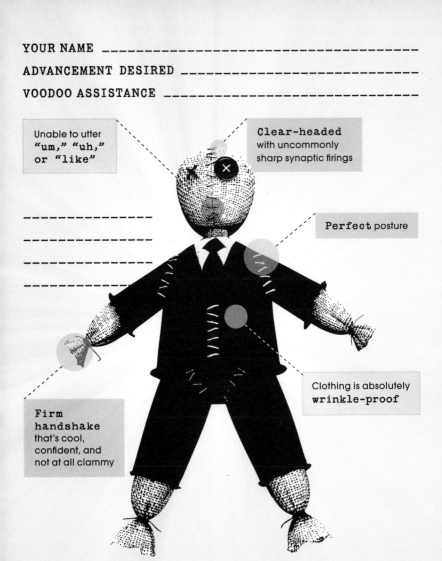

YOUR NAME _____

ADVANCEMENT DESIRED _____

VOODOO ASSISTANCE _____

Unable to utter
**"um," "uh,"
or "like"**

Clear-headed
with uncommonly
sharp synaptic firings

_____

_____

_____

_____

Perfect posture

Clothing is absolutely
wrinkle-proof

**Firm
handshake**
that's cool,
confident, and
not at all clammy

*** Check all that apply. Fill in your own spells and incantations. ***

YOUR INCANTATIONS _____

_____

_____

MORE CHARMS _____

_____

_____

_____

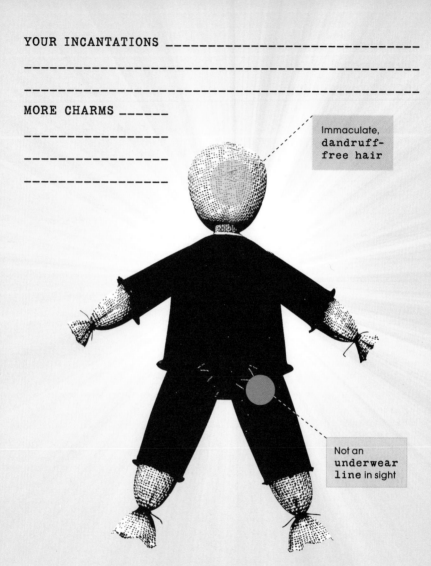

Immaculate, **dandruff-free hair**

Not an **underwear line** in sight

YOUR NAME _____

ADVANCEMENT DESIRED _____

VOODOO ASSISTANCE _____

Unable to utter
"um," "uh,"
or "like"

Clear-headed
with uncommonly
sharp synaptic firings

_____

_____

_____

_____

Perfect posture

Clothing is absolutely
wrinkle-proof

Firm
handshake
that's cool,
confident, and not
at all clammy

*** Check all that apply. Fill in your own spells and incantations. ***

257

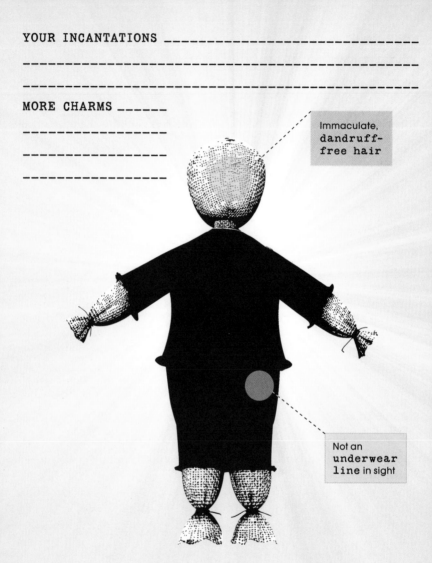

YOUR INCANTATIONS _
_ _
_ _

MORE CHARMS _ _ _ _ _ _
_ _ _ _ _ _ _ _ _ _ _ _ _ _
_ _ _ _ _ _ _ _ _ _ _ _ _ _
_ _ _ _ _ _ _ _ _ _ _ _ _ _

Immaculate,
**dandruff-
free hair**

Not an
**underwear
line** in sight

YOUR NAME _____

ADVANCEMENT DESIRED _____

VOODOO ASSISTANCE _____

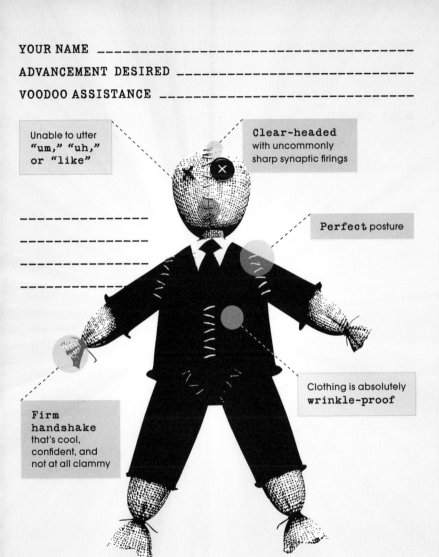

Unable to utter "um," "uh," or "like"

Clear-headed with uncommonly sharp synaptic firings

_____
_____
_____
_____

Perfect posture

Firm handshake that's cool, confident, and not at all clammy

Clothing is absolutely wrinkle-proof

*** Check all that apply. Fill in your own spells and incantations. ***

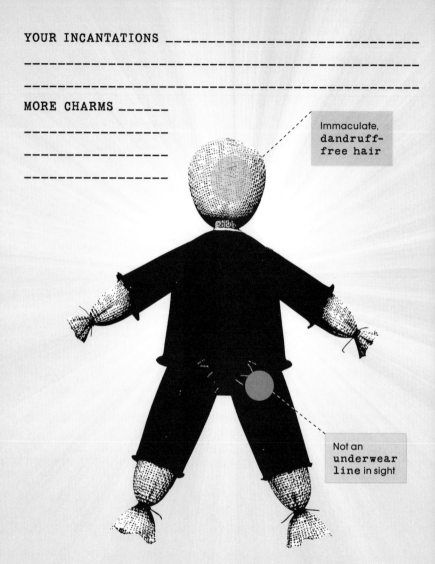

YOUR INCANTATIONS _

MORE CHARMS _ _ _ _ _ _
_ _ _ _ _ _ _ _ _ _ _ _ _ _ _ _
_ _ _ _ _ _ _ _ _ _ _ _ _ _ _ _
_ _ _ _ _ _ _ _ _ _ _ _ _ _ _ _

Immaculate,
**dandruff-
free hair**

Not an
**underwear
line** in sight

YOUR NAME _____

ADVANCEMENT DESIRED _____

VOODOO ASSISTANCE _____

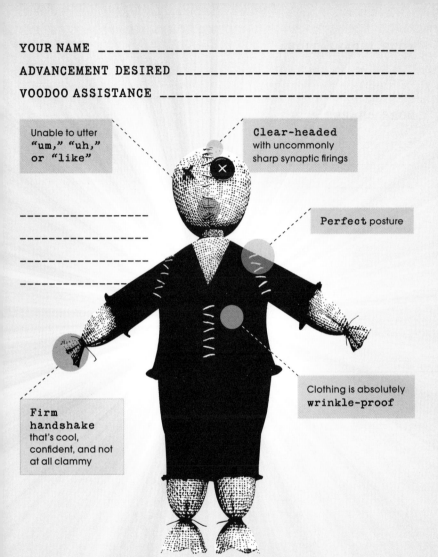

Unable to utter **"um," "uh," or "like"**

Clear-headed with uncommonly sharp synaptic firings

_____
_____
_____
_____

Perfect posture

Firm handshake that's cool, confident, and not at all clammy

Clothing is absolutely **wrinkle-proof**

*** Check all that apply. Fill in your own spells and incantations. ***

MORE CHARMS _ _ _ _ _ _
_ _ _ _ _ _ _ _ _ _ _ _ _ _ _ _
_ _ _ _ _ _ _ _ _ _ _ _ _ _ _ _
_ _ _ _ _ _ _ _ _ _ _ _ _ _ _ _

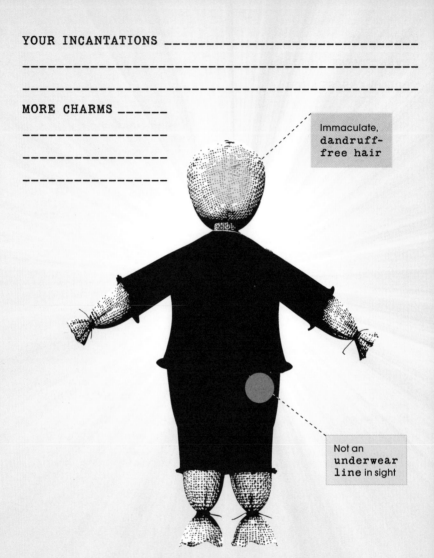

Immaculate, **dandruff-free hair**

Not an **underwear line** in sight

YOUR NAME _____

ADVANCEMENT DESIRED _____

VOODOO ASSISTANCE _____

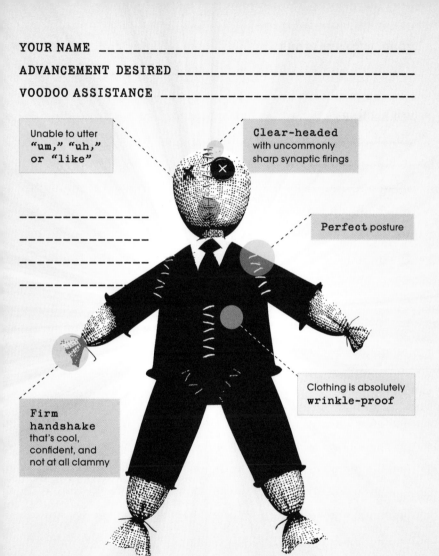

Unable to utter
**"um," "uh,"
or "like"**

Clear-headed
with uncommonly
sharp synaptic firings

_____
_____
_____
_____

Perfect posture

**Firm
handshake**
that's cool,
confident, and
not at all clammy

Clothing is absolutely
wrinkle-proof

*** Check all that apply. Fill in your own spells and incantations. ***

MORE CHARMS _____
_____
_____
_____

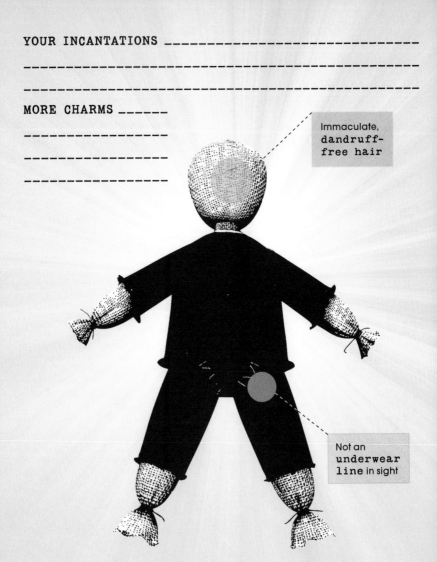

Immaculate, **dandruff-free hair**

Not an **underwear line** in sight

YOUR NAME _____

ADVANCEMENT DESIRED _____

VOODOO ASSISTANCE _____

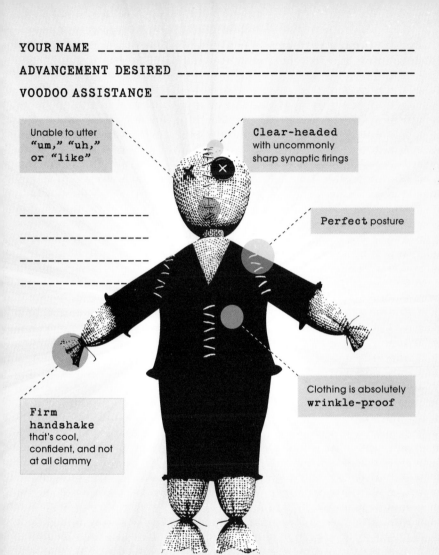

Unable to utter "um," "uh," or "like"

Clear-headed with uncommonly sharp synaptic firings

Perfect posture

_____
_____

_____

_____

Firm handshake that's cool, confident, and not at all clammy

Clothing is absolutely wrinkle-proof

*** Check all that apply. Fill in your own spells and incantations. ***

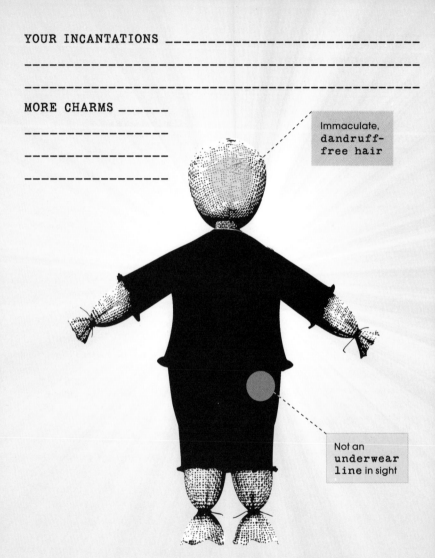

YOUR INCANTATIONS _____
_____
_____

MORE CHARMS _ _ _ _ _ _
_ _ _ _ _ _ _ _ _ _ _ _ _ _ _ _
_ _ _ _ _ _ _ _ _ _ _ _ _ _ _ _
_ _ _ _ _ _ _ _ _ _ _ _ _ _ _ _

Immaculate, **dandruff-free hair**

Not an **underwear line** in sight

YOUR NAME _____

ADVANCEMENT DESIRED _____

VOODOO ASSISTANCE _____

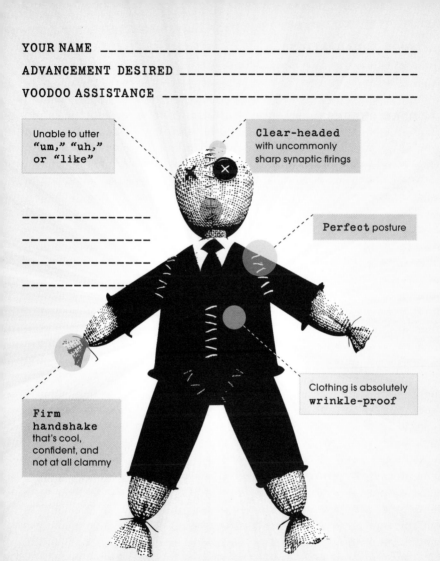

Unable to utter **"um," "uh," or "like"**

Clear-headed with uncommonly sharp synaptic firings

_____
_____
_____
_____

Perfect posture

Clothing is absolutely **wrinkle-proof**

Firm handshake that's cool, confident, and not at all clammy

*** Check all that apply. Fill in your own spells and incantations. ***

YOUR INCANTATIONS _____

_____

_____

MORE CHARMS _____

_____

_____

_____

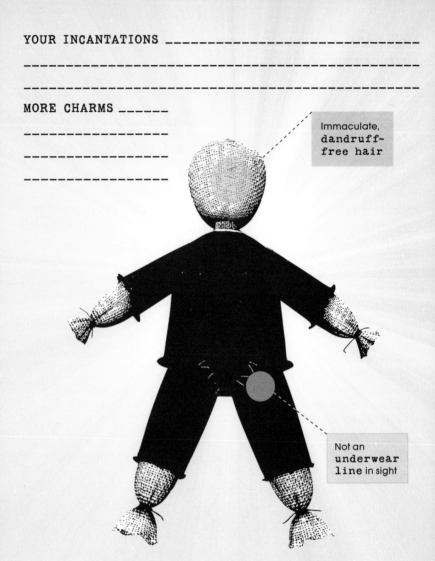

Immaculate, **dandruff-free hair**

Not an **underwear line** in sight

268

YOUR NAME _____

ADVANCEMENT DESIRED _____

VOODOO ASSISTANCE _____

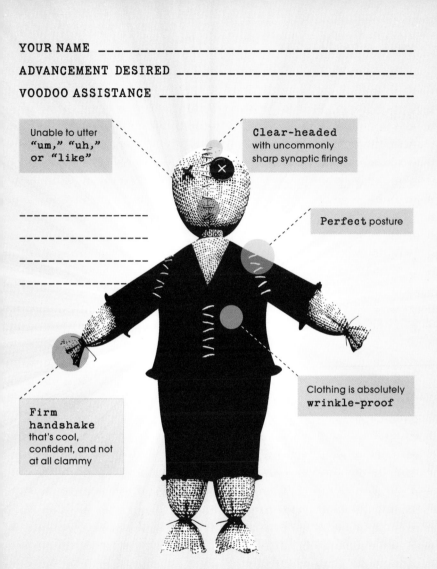

Unable to utter
"um," "uh,"
or "like"

Clear-headed
with uncommonly
sharp synaptic firings

_____
_____
_____
_____

Perfect posture

**Firm
handshake**
that's cool,
confident, and not
at all clammy

Clothing is absolutely
wrinkle-proof

*** Check all that apply. Fill in your own spells and incantations. ***

YOUR INCANTATIONS _____
_____
_____

MORE CHARMS _____
_____
_____
_____

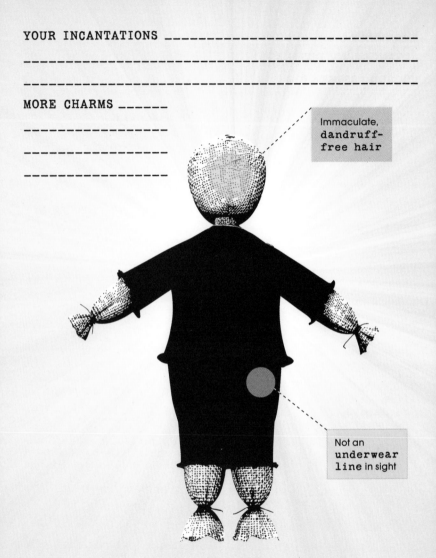

Immaculate, **dandruff-free hair**

Not an **underwear line** in sight

YOUR NAME _____

ADVANCEMENT DESIRED _____

VOODOO ASSISTANCE _____

Unable to utter
**"um," "uh,"
or "like"**

Clear-headed
with uncommonly
sharp synaptic firings

_____
_____
_____
_____

Perfect posture

Clothing is absolutely
wrinkle-proof

**Firm
handshake**
that's cool,
confident, and
not at all clammy

*** Check all that apply. Fill in your own spells and incantations. ***

271

YOUR INCANTATIONS _____

_____

_____

MORE CHARMS _____

_____

_____

_____

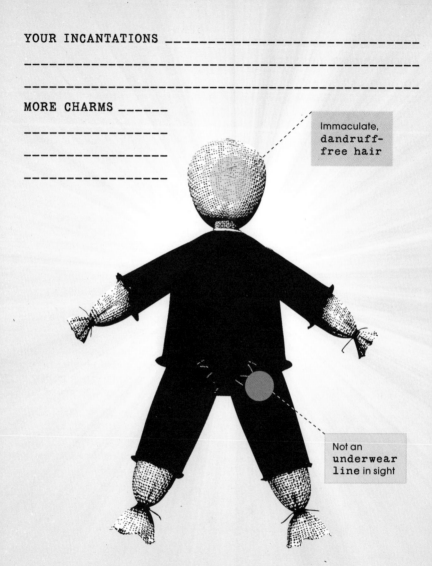

Immaculate,
**dandruff-
free hair**

Not an
**underwear
line** in sight